PHYSICAL CHEMISTRY
FOR BIOLOGISTS AND MEDICAL STUDENTS

AN INTRODUCTION TO
PHYSICAL CHEMISTRY

for Biologists and Medical Students with special reference to Colloid Chemistry

By

H. R. KRUYT

Formerly Professor at the University of Utrecht

and

J. T. G. OVERBEEK

Professor at the University of Utrecht

Translated by

A. J. MEE

in collaboration with

J. E. SPICE

HOLT, RINEHART AND WINSTON, INC.

New York   1964

FIRST PUBLISHED 1960
REPRINTED 1964

Library of Congress Catalog Card Number : 62–9972

25054–0112

Printed in Great Britain

PREFACE

This book, as its title indicates, is written especially to present the fundamentals of physical chemistry to such depth as is required by medical students and biologists. Students of physical chemistry as such will no doubt be disappointed with the contents of the book; they might rightly have expected to find up-to-date theories of atomic structure, and applications of thermodynamics to chemistry, but the book is not intended for them. Broadly speaking the book deals with those aspects of physical chemistry which are necessary for the understanding of colloid science, and with elementary colloid science itself.

No better author could have been found for a work of this type than Dr. H. R. Kruyt. He is widely known as an authority on colloid chemistry, and the original of the present book has already run into fifteen editions in Holland. In fact, the preparation of this translation was begun some years ago, and was just finished when a new Dutch edition appeared which necessitated a substantial revision of the translation, thus delaying publication in this country. The popularity of the book in Holland makes it obvious that it has been of considerable use to University students of biology and medicine in that country, and it is hoped that it will prove of equal value to such students in the English-speaking nations.

In the preparation of this translation I have been greatly helped by Dr. J. E. Spice, formerly of the University of Liverpool and now of Winchester College, Dr. G. A. Gilbert, of the University of Birmingham, and Dr. A. Tanfield of St. Mary's Hospital Medical School, who read the manuscript and made many valuable suggestions which have been incorporated in the text.

A. J. M.

CONTENTS

CHAPTER I

PROPERTIES OF SOLUTIONS
OSMOTIC PRESSURE

IN this chapter the phenomenon of osmotic pressure will be dealt with. With that end in view we shall discuss first Boyle's law, then the kinetic theory of gases, the conception of molecular weight, the Brownian movement, and, finally, osmotic pressure.

1. Boyle's Law

The connection between the pressure (P) and the volume (V) of a gas is familiar from elementary work in science. The relationship is given by Boyle's law which states that for a given mass of gas the product of the pressure and volume is constant if the temperature is constant. Charles' law in combination with Boyle's law states that

$$PV = RT$$

where T is the absolute temperature, and R is the so-called gas constant. Since the constant R plays an important part in many types of calculation, it is worth-while to work out its value. It is obvious that the value of R will depend on the units in which P and V are expressed.

The mass of gas to be considered in the calculation has first to be decided. We could choose 1 kg., but in physical chemistry it is more usual to deal with 1 gram-molecule (or mole). If, in any particular case, n moles are considered, the equation becomes

$$PV = nRT.$$

It will be remembered from elementary work that 1 mole of a gas at 0° C. and 1 atmosphere pressure occupies a volume of 22·4 litres. We can calculate R by substituting these figures in the equation

$$PV = RT.$$

We then have

$$1 \times 22 \cdot 4 = R \times 273$$
$$R = \frac{22 \cdot 4}{273} = 0 \cdot 0821 \ \frac{\text{litre-atmospheres per}}{\text{mole per } °\text{K}}$$

To express this result in C.G.S. units we note that a pressure of 1 atmosphere is the pressure exerted by a column of mercury at 0°C. (density 13·6 g. per c.c.) 76 cm. long. Thus

1 atmosphere pressure $= 76 \times 13\cdot6 \times 981$ dynes per sq. cm. (since
$$g = 981 \text{ cm. per sec. per sec.})$$
$$= 1\cdot014 \times 10^6 \text{ dynes per sq. cm.}$$
22·4 litres $= 22\cdot4 \times 10^3$ c.c.

Hence $1\cdot014 \times 10^6 \times 22\cdot4 \times 10^3 = 273R$
$$R = 8\cdot31 \times 10^7 \underline{\text{ergs per mole per } °K.}$$

To convert this value in ergs to calories we make use of the mechanical equivalent of heat :

1 calorie is equivalent to $4\cdot185 \times 10^7$ ergs.

Hence $R = 2$ cals. per mole per °K. (or, more accurately, $\underline{1\cdot986}$ cals. per mole per °K.

Sometimes it is desirable to express R in electrical units. Since 1 volt $\times$ 1 coulomb ($= 1$ joule) is equivalent to 10^7 ergs, we can write 8·31 joules instead of $8\cdot31 \times 10^7$ ergs. for R.

Summarizing we see that R can be expressed as

0·0821 litre-atmospheres per mole per °K.,
$8\cdot31 \times 10^7$ ergs per mole per °K.,
8·31 joules per mole per °K.,
or 1·986 cals. per mole per °K.

Sometimes the gas constant is calculated not for a gram-molecule but for a single molecule. We shall find out on p. 7 how many molecules are contained in a gram-molecule (Avogadro's number) ; suppose we call this N. If the gas constant for 1 molecule is calculated (instead of for a gram-molecule) it is denoted not by R but by k. It is obvious that in this case $k = R/N$. k is known as the Boltzmann constant.

2. Kinetic Theory

Let us recall how Boyle's law is deduced in elementary science on the basis of the kinetic theory of gases.

Fig. 1 represents a section of a cube of side 1 cm. Suppose the mass of gas contained within the cube is M, and let it contain n molecules, each of mass m. Suppose further that each molecule moves with a speed of c cm. per sec. The pressure exerted on one wall in consequence of the collisions of the n molecules against the wall is then calculated. The molecules, of course, are constantly colliding with each other, as well as with the wall. However, if all collisions are assumed to be perfectly elastic, the inter-molecular collisions may be disregarded, and the situation is then as shown

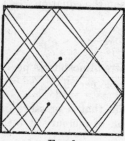

Fig. 1.

in Fig. 1.   By resolving the velocity in three directions mutually at right angles, the collisions may be regarded as due to the contact with the walls of three streams of molecules, the molecules in a stream moving to and fro in one of the three mutually perpendicular directions.   Let us follow the motion of one of the molecules in one of the streams. This molecule will strike each wall at right angles to its path $\frac{1}{2}c$ times a second. The momentum of the molecule will be changed by $2mc$ at each collision, since the velocity is first reduced to zero as the molecule strikes the wall, and then the molecule moves away from the wall with a velocity c, the collision being perfectly elastic. The force exerted on the wall by the single molecule considered s thus $2mc \times \frac{1}{2}c$, this being the rate of change of momentum. The pressure on the wall arising from all collisions by molecules in the stream perpendicular to the wall thus amounts to *

$$P = n/3 \times \tfrac{1}{2}c \times 2mc$$
$$= \tfrac{1}{3}nmc^2,$$
$$\text{or } P = \tfrac{1}{3}Mc^2.$$

If the cube has a volume V c.c. this equation becomes

$$PV = \tfrac{1}{3}Mc^2.$$

This result makes it possible to calculate the velocity of the molecules of a gas. Thus, 1 c.c. of oxygen at 0° C. and 760 mm. pressure weighs $32/22400 = 0\cdot00143$ gm. Since a pressure of 760 mm. of mercury is equivalent to one of $1\cdot014 \times 10^6$ dynes per sq. cm. (p. 2), we have

$$1\cdot014 \times 10^6 = \tfrac{1}{3} \times 0\cdot00143 \times c^2,$$
$$\text{or } c = 461 \text{ metres per second.}$$

In the same way, the molecular velocities at N.T.P. for nitrogen and hydrogen are respectively 493 and 1839 metres per second.

It must be emphasized that these figures refer to the velocity of the molecules and not to their displacement. The molecules actually execute a random, zig-zag motion on account of their collisions with each other, so, notwithstanding these high speeds, their actual displacement is relatively small. We shall return to this difference between velocity and displacement later (p. 6).

As shown above, the relationship

$$PV = \tfrac{1}{3}Mc^2$$

---

* If it is assumed that instead of a cube of volume 1 c.c., we have a cylinder with a cross-sectional area a^2 sq. cm., and height b cm., the calculation becomes

$$Pa^2 = \tfrac{1}{3}n \times \frac{c}{2b} \times 2mc$$

a^2b is, however, the volume of the cylinder V. Hence

$$PV = \tfrac{1}{3}Mc^2$$
$$\text{and } RT = \tfrac{1}{3}Mc^2$$

holds for any gas. As we know from experiment, $PV = RT$, and consequently the absolute temperature of a gas is proportional to the kinetic energy, $\frac{1}{2}Mc^2$, possessed by its molecules. Thus, for two gases at the same temperature the products Mc^2, but not the molecular speeds c, are equal. It thus follows from the above equation that the volume of a given mass of gas is inversely proportional to its pressure if the temperature is constant (Boyle's law), and that the volume of a given mass of gas at constant pressure is proportional to its absolute temperature (Charles' law).

One correction must be made to what has been said above. The molecules of a gas do not all have the same velocity, nor does any given molecule have a constant velocity. As a result of molecular collisions molecular velocities are constantly changing. At a given temperature, however, the mean velocity, c, of the molecules, from the above assumption, must be constant. The velocity c is not actually the arithmetic mean of all the individual molecular velocities, but it is the square root of the average of the squares of the molecular velocities :

$$c = \sqrt{\frac{c_1^2 + c_2^2 + c_3^2 + \cdots + c_n^2}{n}}.$$

c is called the root-mean-square velocity, and is often given the symbol $\bar{u}$.

3. Avogadro's Hypothesis

It is easy to show how Avogadro's hypothesis follows from the above reasoning. This states that equal volumes of different gases, under the same conditions of temperature and pressure, contain the same number of molecules.

Let us consider 1 c.c. of each gas. Since the pressures are the same we can write

$$\tfrac{1}{3}m_1 n_1 \bar{u}_1^2 = \tfrac{1}{3}m_2 n_2 \bar{u}_2^2$$

where the symbols have their usual significance, and the suffixes refer to the two gases, respectively.

Since, moreover, the temperatures are the same, the average kinetic energies of the molecules of the different gases will be the same, and so

$$\tfrac{1}{2}m_1 \bar{u}_1^2 = \tfrac{1}{2}m_2 \bar{u}_2^2.$$

By dividing these last two equations it follows immediately that

$$n_1 = n_2,$$

which is Avogadro's hypothesis. The ratio of the weights of equal volumes of different gases is therefore the ratio of their molecular weights, m_1/m_2. By weighing a given volume of different gases we can thus obtain the ratio of the molecular weights of the gases.

As is well known, we take, in chemistry, the volume of 2 gm. of hydrogen as a unit. At 0° C. and 760 mm. pressure this has a volume of 22·4 litres. In 22·4 litres of any gas there is a fixed number of molecules, which we will call N. Throughout the whole of the nineteenth century the idea of molecular weight (calculated on the basis of that of hydrogen being 2) was used, although the value of N was not known. Lack of knowledge of this fundamental number made many people doubt the whole atomistic basis of chemistry, and also the kinetic theory of gases. During the last sixty years, however, various different lines of experiment have removed all doubt about the existence of atoms and molecules, and have made possible the calculation of N, Avogadro's number, by several distinct methods. One of these lines of experiment is the study of the Brownian movement.

4. The Brownian Movement

The English botanist Robert Brown was the first to notice, in 1827, that particles were present in the pollen grains of certain plants, which when placed in water and observed under the microscope appeared never to remain still, but to be continually executing an irregular, vibratory motion. He thought originally that the movement had something to do with life, but his prolonged investigations showed that all types of material, living and inorganic, gave the same phenomenon, provided the substances were sufficiently finely divided.

During the nineteenth century a number of investigations were carried out by Wiener, Exner and Gouy, and others, with the object of trying to discover the origin of the Brownian movement. All these investigations led to the conclusion that the Brownian movement was not confined to any particular class of matter, but was a general property of substances in a fine state of division. The invention of the ultramicroscope (see p. 118) brought the phenomenon of the Brownian movement again to the fore, because with this apparatus the Brownian movement became more clearly visible and gave unmistakable evidence before one's very eyes of that which the kinetic theory of gases had formerly laid down as hypothesis. The same phenomenon has also been observed in mists, where droplets or solid particles are dispersed in air. If it is correct to regard the Brownian movement as the thermal motion of the visible particles, then, in accordance with the views stated above, it should be possible by this method to obtain the mass of the molecules, and the value of Avogadro's number N. Since the particles and the gas are at the same temperature the kinetic energy of the molecules of the liquid or gas in which the particles executing the Brownian movement are suspended must be the same as that of the suspended particles. There is an equilibrium between the two. Hence

$$(\tfrac{1}{2}mc^2)_{\text{Brownian particles}} = (\tfrac{1}{2}mc^2)_{\text{molecules}} \quad \cdots \quad (1)$$

In this equation the velocity of the gas molecules is known, according to the calculation given in § 2. The mass, m, of the moving particles can be obtained by Stokes' law. This states that the fractional force, w, acting on a spherical particle moving in a liquid, is given by

$$w = 6\pi\eta rs$$

where η is the viscosity of the liquid, r the radius of the particle, and s the velocity with which it moves. If the particle is allowed to fall through the liquid under the action of gravity the value of r can be obtained from the observation of s, and r is a measure of m. We thus have

$$\frac{4}{3}\pi r^3(d_p - d_m)g = 6\pi\eta rs,$$

where d_p is the density of the particle, d_m that of the medium through which it falls, and g is the acceleration due to gravity. If now, the velocity, v, of the particles executing the Brownian movement can be measured, then all the quantities in equation (1) except the mass of the molecule are known, and the latter can therefore be calculated.

It now remains to determine the velocity of the particles carrying out the Brownian movement. Numerous attempts to do this by direct observation, either by eye or by means of cinematography, have been made. These observations, however, give uncertain or improbable results. In the year 1904 Einstein and von Smoluchowski, working independently of each other, discovered a method of obtaining an accurate result. The velocity of a particle should be determined by measuring the zig-zag path which the particle covers in a fixed time ; it is, however, obvious, that the particle traverses a much more intricate path than would appear to the eye. Indeed calculation has shown that it is very probable that a particle changes its course as frequently as ten million times a second. It is thus out of the question to determine the speed of the particle by trying to follow its path by eye. There is, however, another quantity which it is quite possible to measure, namely its displacement.

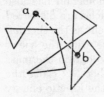

If a particle moves completely arbitrarily in the midst of millions of other particles, it is, of course, impossible to say just where a given particle will be after a certain time. It is clear, however, that the probability that a particle shall be further from its starting point is greater the longer one watches. Investigations based on

FIG. 2.

By counting the scintillations it is found that 1 gm. of radium gives $3\cdot4 \times 10^{10}$ scintillations per second which arise only from the first stage of the disintegration. In a year, and with four stages of disintegration this amounts to

$$3\cdot4 \times 10^{10} \times 4 \times 60 \times 60 \times 24 \times 365 = 4\cdot29 \times 10^{18} \text{ atoms of helium.}$$

Avogadro's number is found by dividing the number of atoms by the number of gm.-atoms, thus :

$$N = \frac{4\cdot29 \times 10^{18}}{6\cdot96 \times 10^{-6}} = 6\cdot15 \times 10^{23}.$$

The best value for Avogadro's number is probably $N = 6\cdot0235 \times 10^{23}$, and has been obtained by yet another method, depending on the calculation of the density of crystalline potassium chloride from the distance between the potassium and chloride ions, obtained by X-ray diffraction measurements.

6. Diffusion

Fig. 3 shows two spaces A and B, which can be connected with each other, and which we may suppose contain initially the same gas. The separating line in the diagram is thus, for the time being, imaginary. Consider 1 sq. cm. of the imaginary plane of separation.

Since we suppose that the two volumes of gas are in equilibrium with each other, we may assume, on the basis of the kinetic theory of gases, that the same number of molecules will pass from A to B as pass from B to A over a square centimetre of the dividing surface in the same period of time. This conception of equilibrium does not, therefore, regard it as static, but as dynamic; there are two similar but opposite motions.

FIG. 3.

If we consider one gas in A and a different one in B, both under the same conditions of temperature and pressure, there will be displacement of the molecules through the imaginary separating plane. In this case, however, these displacements do not compensate each other, for molecules of A go from left to right, and molecules of B from right to left.

This phenomenon is diffusion ; it takes place until a state of affairs is reached when the same number of molecules of A pass from right to left as pass from left to right across each square centimetre of the dividing wall per unit time, and as many molecules of B pass from left to right as pass from right to left, under the same conditions. It is obvious that this will be the case only when the two gases are homogeneously mixed. Diffusion thus ends when the gas mixture becomes completely homogeneous

If now we think of a liquid in A and another liquid in B, diffusion takes place in exactly the same manner as described above for gases.

Suppose we have water in A, and water in which, say, sugar has been dissolved, in B. Through unit surface of the dividing plane there now pass both water and sugar molecules, water in both directions, sugar, for the time being, only from right to left. It is clear that diffusion will go on in this case until all the sugar is distributed homogeneously throughout the two compartments.

Let us now suppose that a solution of concentration c_1 is placed in A, and one of concentration c_2 in B. Diffusion must again take place, but although it is true that sugar and water molecules travel in both directions the ratio of sugar to water in the two compartments is different, and the conditions for dynamic equilibrium are not fulfilled.

How rapidly does this diffusion take place ? It is easy to see that if we consider for a moment the quantity of substance dm which passes through the partition in a very short time, this will be proportional to the area of the separating surface (q), the concentration gradient on the two sides of the partition *, and the time during which the diffusion process takes place, dt. The relationship is expressed by Fick's law, which, in mathematical terms states that

$$dm = -Dq\frac{dc}{dx}.\,dt$$

where D is a proportionality factor called the diffusion constant or coefficient. It is clearly the mass of substance which diffuses through unit area of surface in unit time when there is unit concentration gradient. This diffusion constant varies, of course, from one substance to another.

It is obvious that a close relationship must exist between the diffusion constant and the displacement, $\overline{\Delta}$, with which we dealt in the previous paragraph.

Consider three equidistant planes, a, b, and c (Fig. 4) in the solution. Their area is q and the distance between each is $\overline{\Delta}$, the mean displacement of the diffusing molecules in time t. Half the molecules in compartment 1 will pass through the surface a to the left and the other half will pass through the surface b to

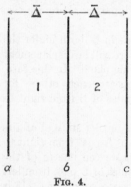

Fig. 4.

* By concentration gradient is understood the rate of change of concentration with distance. Thus, if the difference in concentration at two places at a distance dx apart is dc, the concentration gradient is dc/dx.

the right. Similarly for the molecules in compartment 2. The net transport through b in t seconds is thus

$$\mathrm{d}m = \tfrac{1}{2}q\Delta c_1 - \tfrac{1}{2}q\overline{\Delta}c_2$$

where c_1 and c_2 are the mean concentrations (or the concentration in the middle) of the compartments 1 and 2, respectively.

This equation can also be written

$$\mathrm{d}m = \frac{\overline{\Delta}^2}{2t} \cdot q \cdot \frac{c_1 - c_2}{\overline{\Delta}} \cdot t$$

$(c_1 - c_2)/\overline{\Delta}$ is the same as the concentration gradient $\mathrm{d}c/\mathrm{d}x$. For small intervals of time we may write $\mathrm{d}t$ for t. From equation (2) on p. 7 we see that $\overline{\Delta}^2/2t$ is constant, and this constant is clearly the diffusion constant D from Fick's law. Hence

$$D = \frac{\overline{\Delta}^2}{2t} = \frac{RT}{N} \cdot \frac{1}{6\pi\eta r}.$$

It is thus seen that the diffusion constant, D, is inversely proportional to r, the radius of the diffusing molecule. The size of a molecule is naturally connected with the molecular weight. In the table below the molecular weights and diffusion constants of some substances are given. It is seen that a larger molecular weight is accompanied by a smaller diffusion constant.

	Molecular weight	D cm. per day
Urea . . .	60	0·81
Chloral hydrate . .	165	0·59
Mannitol . . .	182	0·40
Cane sugar . .	342	0·31
Haemoglobin . .	63000	0·059

7. Osmosis

We have already considered the case where compartment A (Fig. 3) contains water and compartment B a sugar solution. The dividing wall between the two compartments may be supposed to be made of filter paper which is permeable to both water and sugar. We have seen that the two molecular species move through the dividing wall until there is a homogeneous distribution of sugar throughout the two compartments.

Let us now suppose that the filter paper is replaced by an animal membrane which has the property of allowing the water molecules to pass through, but not the sugar. The motion of the sugar molecules through the membrane thus no longer comes into consideration ; there is none. What happens then to the movement of the water molecules ? On a square centimetre of the dividing surface there are only water molecules on the left, but on the right there are some water molecules and some sugar molecules. More water molecules hit the dividing membrane on the left than on the right in the same time. In unit time, therefore, more water molecules will pass from A to B than from B to A. The consequence is, therefore, a streaming of water from the water side to the solution side. Is it possible for this unidirectional current to be counteracted ? The answer is that the excess water molecules in B exert an excess pressure, which eventually becomes great enough to cause just as many water molecules to pass from B to A in a given time as are passing from A to B. This excess pressure is called osmotic pressure.

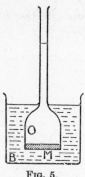

FIG. 5.

The process here outlined is exactly that which takes place in the osmometer (Fig. 5)

Here O is a sugar solution, and B is water. The level in the tube rises, indicating the passage of water molecules into the osmometer. As soon as a certain pressure has been reached (measured by the height of the liquid in the tube) there is no further net flow of water ; that is to say, a state of equilibrium arises in which the pressure of the water molecules on the membrane M causes just sufficient molecules of water to pass back to compensate for those passing in.

In order to avoid the complications of hydrostatic pressure and of concentration changes due to incoming water we may consider an osmometer of the type shown in Fig. 6, where Z is a piston, which may be supposed to be capable of moving in its socket without friction. Weights can be placed on it in order to apply pressure to counterbalance the hydrostatic pressure. The osmotic pressure would thus be measured as the weight per square centimetre that must be applied to the piston in order just to prevent water from entering the osmometer. How great is the pressure required to prevent the water from flowing in ?

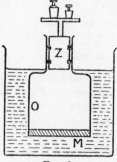

FIG. 6.

The answer was given by van't Hoff in the form of a law which may be stated as follows :

The osmotic pressure has the same value as the gas pressure which the dissolved substance would exert if it existed as a gas occupying the same volume as the solution. It must, however, be clearly understood that osmotic pressure is by no means identical with gas pressure in origin. The usual conception of osmotic pressure as if it were the direct consequence of the kinetic energy of the molecules of the solute, as gas pressure is in the case of molecules of a gas, is thus entirely incorrect.

From what has been said the gas equation will evidently apply also to osmotic pressure. That is,

$$PV = nRT$$

or

$$P = \frac{nRT}{V}.$$

$\frac{n}{V}$, the number of gram-molecules divided by the volume in which they are contained, is the concentration of the solution. If we write c for $\frac{n}{V}$ and π in place of P in order to show that we are dealing with osmotic pressure and not gas pressure, we have

$$\pi = RTc \quad \ldots \ldots \ldots \quad (3)$$

as the mathematical expression for the law of van't Hoff.

Suppose it is desired to calculate the value of the osmotic pressure exerted by a 1 per cent. solution of glucose when it is separated from pure water by a semi-permeable membrane. The following method is used :

A 1 per cent. solution of glucose contains 10 gm. per litre. The molecular weight of glucose is 180. The concentration is thus $\frac{1}{18}$ gm.-mol. per litre, or 1 gm.-mol. in 18 litres. One gm.-mol. in 22·4 litres gives an osmotic pressure of 1 atmosphere at 0° C. Hence our glucose solution would give an osmotic pressure of

$$\frac{22\cdot4}{18} = 1\cdot25 \text{ atmospheres.}$$

This is correct at 0° C. If we wish to calculate the osmotic pressure at room temperature, say 15° C. (288° Abs.), we have

$$\frac{1\cdot25 \times 288}{273} = 1\cdot25 \times 1\cdot055 = 1\cdot32 \text{ atmospheres.}$$

The same result would be arrived at by substituting in equation (3), remembering that $R = 0\cdot0821$ when the pressure is measured in atmospheres and the concentration in gram-molecules per litre (see p. 1),

$$\pi = \frac{0 \cdot 0821 \times 288}{18}$$

$$= 1 \cdot 32 \text{ atmospheres.}$$

From the foregoing discussion it should be quite clear that it is irrational to talk of the osmotic pressure of a solution. An isolated solution never has an osmotic pressure. Osmotic pressure is fundamentally a compensation for a unidirectional flow of water when a solution is separated from the solvent (water) by a semi-permeable wall. If such an expression as " a solution of 1 atmosphere osmotic pressure " must be used, it must be clearly understood that this is not equivalent to the expression " a gas at 1 atmosphere pressure," but is an ellipsis, such as " a motor of 5 h.p.," or " a lad of 12 years."

The osmotic pressure need not necessarily be calculated with respect to the pure solvent. Two solutions of different concentrations of the same solute can be used, or two solutions of different substances. If two solutions have the same osmotic pressure they are said to be *isotonic solutions* ; if the osmotic pressure of one of them is less than that of the other it is said to be *hypotonic* ; if it is greater, the solution is *hypertonic*.

Just as Boyle's law holds good only for gases at low pressure (" dilute " gases), so van't Hoff's law only holds with accuracy for dilute solutions. This is illustrated in the table below, which gives the results of accurate determinations of the osmotic pressure of sugar solutions carried out by two American workers, Morse and Frazer.

Concentration	0°	20°	40°	60°
0·1	—	1·05	1·00	1·00
0·3	1·06	1·06	1·02	1·00
0·5	1·07	1·07	1·05	1·01
0·8	1·09	1·09	1·07	1·03
1·0	1·12	1·12	1·09	1·04

The table gives a comparison of the observed and calculated values of the osmotic pressure of solutions, of which the concentrations are given in gram-molecules per litre. The value 1·00 means that the measured and calculated values agree. From the table it is seen that at 40° and 60° there is a certain measure of agreement with the most dilute solutions, but that at 20° even for a solution containing only 0·1 gm.-mol. per litre there is a deviation of 5 per cent. Modifications in the law of van't Hoff, similar to van der Waals' equation, have repeatedly been put forward.

In our discussion of osmotic pressure we have assumed the existence of a semi-permeable membrane. Is there such a thing ? As is well known pig's bladder is more or less satisfactory for this purpose, but many experiments on osmotic pressure have been carried out with porous pots in the pores of which copper ferrocyanide has been deposited. Inside the pot is placed a solution of copper sulphate, $CuSO_4$, and outside is a solution of potassium ferrocyanide, $K_4Fe(CN)_6$. Copper ferrocyanide, $Cu_2Fe(CN)_6$, is deposited in the pores where the two solutions meet, and serves very well as a semi-permeable membrane.

For the *theory* of osmotic pressure the existence of such a semi-permeable wall is actually unnecessary. Also the nature of the membrane is not important, or we should not have been able to deal with this phenomenon in the way we have above. We must now consider the mechanism by which a semi-permeable membrane may function.

It might at first be supposed that a type of sieve action takes place. Nevertheless this view is not very satisfactory, and the mechanism appears to be rather different. If, for example, a solution of benzene in ether is separated from pure ether by means of a cork saturated with water, the water appears to function as a semi-permeable membrane. Ether is soluble in water, but benzene is not ; consequently the water allows the ether to pass through, but not the benzene.

Osmosis in gases can be demonstrated in a similar way. In Fig. 7, K is a vessel which is closed with a piece of flannel, L, which is saturated with water. Ammonia gas is passed into the surrounding beaker B. The ammonia dissolves in the water in the flannel when it reaches the vessel. The air, however, dissolves much less rapidly in the water so that no air passes through the flannel. The ammonia gas entering thus makes the pressure rise and the manometer, to which the vessel is connected, indicates the change. This experiment is exactly comparable with the osmometer experiment in Figs. 5 and 6. The air takes the place of the contents of the osmometer, the ammonia plays the part of the outer liquid. The

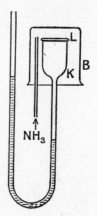

Fig. 7.

semi-permeability of the wet piece of flannel, which allows the ammonia to pass through but not the air, is comparable with that of the pig's bladder. This experiment also illustrates the point that there can be no doubt that the increase of pressure is due to the ammonia molecules (the water molecules in the case of the osmotic experiment) and not the air molecules (the sugar molecules of the osmotic experiment).

From these two examples one might conclude that the mechanism of the semi-permeable membrane is a question of selective solubility. We shall return to other possible explanations later (pp. 168–170), but from these examples it appears that a sieve action by itself is not the only possibility.

We must now enquire into the state of affairs when the wall is not perfectly semi-permeable, i.e., when it allows one constituent to pass through rapidly and the other slowly. For instance, let us suppose that the membrane of Fig. 5 allows sugar molecules to pass through, but more slowly than water molecules. There will now be an initial rise in the level of the solution in the osmometer as water molecules pass through, but the level will gradually fall again as sugar molecules travel (more slowly) in the reverse direction. Thus, the final (equilibrium) state will be that for which both solutions—inside and outside—have the same composition. In other words, for osmosis proper the solvent has a finite diffusion constant through the membrane and the solute has zero diffusion constant, while for the case just considered the two constituents have finite, but different, diffusion constants.

That a difference in velocity of diffusion can give rise to a disturbance

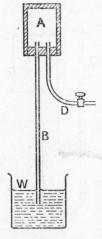

FIG. 8.

of the kinetic equilibrium is easily shown in the case of gases by an experiment described by Graham in 1861.

In Fig. 8, A is a porous pot, and B a vertical tube which passes below the surface of the water W. Hydrogen passes into the porous pot through the tube D. So long as the supply of gas is maintained the hydrogen partly passes through the walls of the porous pot and partly bubbles through the water. If, however, the gas supply is cut off by turning the tap in the tube D, the lighter, and therefore more rapidly moving, hydrogen molecules pass more rapidly through the walls of the porous pot than do the heavier air molecules which come in from outside to take the place of the hydrogen molecules. Consequently water rises in the tube B, and then slowly falls again. It is thus clear how a difference in velocities of diffusion can give rise to phenomena quite in agreement with those observed with osmotic pressure when the membrane is not perfectly semi-permeable.

Since water molecules will pass much more easily through parchment paper than will sugar molecules [although these too appear to pass through after a sufficiently long time (see p. 116)], it is possible to show the phenomenon of osmotic pressure with a sugar solution in an osmometer fitted with a parchment membrane.

If, however, solutions of (say) potassium chloride and magnesium sulphate having the same osmotic pressure (so-called " isotonic " solutions) are separated from each other by a parchment paper membrane, osmosis apparently takes place. This is simply the consequence of the fact that these two salts have different diffusion constants.

We have drawn attention to these various phenomena because it is necessary to emphasize the fact that phenomena which seem to indicate osmotic pressure do not by any means all belong to the type for which the law of van't Hoff holds. Summarizing we can say that osmotic phenomena occur so long as there is a difference in velocity of diffusion through the membrane ; and that van't Hoff's law only holds when one of the diffusion velocities is zero. In biological investigations it is necessary to bear this distinction in mind.

8. Vapour Pressure Lowering and Elevation of Boiling Point

In Fig. 9, A represents water, and B the saturated water vapour with which it is in equilibrium. The characteristic of this state of equilibrium is that for every square centimetre of the water surface as many molecules leave A for B (i.e., vaporize) in unit time, as leave B and pass into A in the same time (i.e., condense).

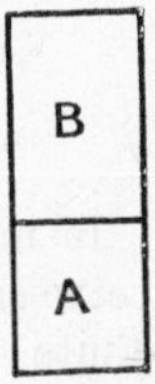

Let us suppose that the water in A is replaced by a solution of sugar in water at the same temperature. Let us consider further the same water vapour in the space B as before. We then have the same problem arising as we had in the previous paragraph. Since in the sugar solution some water molecules have been replaced by sugar molecules, fewer water molecules will evaporate from the surface than will condense in unit time. For the attainment of equilibrium between water vapour and the sugar solution it is therefore necessary that fewer water molecules should be present in the vapour B, or, in other words, the vapour pressure of a solution must be less than that of the pure solvent at the same temperature.

FIG. 9.

The lowering of the vapour pressure is given for dilute solutions by Raoult's law :

$$\frac{p_o - p}{p_o} = \frac{n}{N + n}$$

where p_o is the vapour pressure of the solvent, p that of the solution, n is the number of molecules (or gram-molecules) of solute, and N of solvent. The vapour pressure lowering thus furnishes a method of comparing molecular weights. If 1 gm.-mol. of different substances is dissolved in separate portions of 100 gm. of water the vapour pressure lowering would be the same in all cases, at least if, provisionally, we do not include acids, bases, or salts within the scope of our investigations (this point will be dealt with more fully on p. 60).

However, the experimental determination of vapour pressures is fairly difficult to carry out. Instead the elevation of the boiling point or the depression of the freezing point * is more often measured.

The boiling point is, of course, the temperature at which the vapour pressure of a liquid reaches 1 atmosphere. As the dissolved substance lowers the vapour pressure it is necessary to heat the solution to a higher temperature than is the case with the pure solvent before its vapour pressure reaches 1 atmosphere. The elevation of boiling point which occurs when 1 gm.-mol. of a substance is dissolved in 100 gm. of the solute is called the molecular elevation, Δ. The molecular elevation is different for each solvent, and some values for common solvents are given in the table below.

Solvent	Δ	Solvent	Δ
Water . .	5·12°	Benzene . .	25·3°
Ethyl acetate .	27·7°	Carbon disulphide	23·4°
Chloroform .	36·3°	Ether . . .	20·2°

It must be remembered that there is only strict proportionality between concentration and elevation of boiling point in the case of dilute solutions. The values of the molecular elevation are therefore calculated from the elevation of the boiling point of very dilute solutions, the elevation amounting in these cases at the most to a tenth of a degree. If 1 gm.-mol. of a solute were actually to be dissolved in 100 gm. of solvent the solution would be so concentrated that the law, which applies only to dilute solutions, would no longer hold.

It can be shown by means of thermodynamics that the molecular elevation of the boiling point, Δ, is connected with the latent heat of vaporization of the solvent. van't Hoff deduced the following formula for this relationship :

$$100 \, \Delta = \frac{RT^2}{Q}$$

where Q is the latent heat of vaporization per gram of the solvent, T is the boiling point of the solvent on the absolute scale, and R is the gas constant.

The determination of the molecular weight of a substance by the

* The methods of measurement of molecular weights by elevation of the boiling point and depression of the freezing point to be described in the following paragraphs are called the ebullioscopic and cryoscopic methods, respectively.

method of elevation of the boiling point is often carried out by Landsberger's method (Fig. 10). The inner tube A contains the solution of which the boiling point is to be determined. Bubbles of vapour from the boiling solvent pass into the solution and heat it to the boiling point ; when this steady temperature is reached the thermometer is read. Excess vapour passes into the outer space B and thus forms a blanket around the inner tube, preventing loss of heat by radiation and eliminating the possibility of superheating. The experiment is repeated with the pure solvent

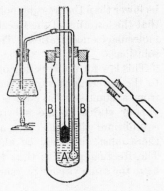

Fig. 10.

in A, the difference between the two temperatures being the required elevation of the boiling point. The thermometer used in this experiment was devised by Beckmann and has a special arrangement by which it can be used for different temperature ranges, although the scale (which is graduated in hundredths of a degree) extends over only a few degrees.

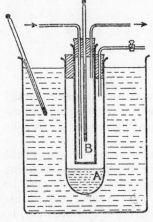

Fig. 11.

For liquids which foam very easily, such as soap solution, it is more convenient to determine the *dew point*. An apparatus due to McBain (Fig. 11) is very suitable for this purpose.

The solution under investigation is contained in the tube A which is placed in a constant temperature bath (a thermostat). A polished silver tube B, through which passes water whose temperature can be altered, is placed in the vapour of the solution. The temperature of the water flowing through the silvered tube is determined when the vapour just begins to condense (formation of dew) on the outside of the tube. The difference in temperature between the liquid in A and the silver tube B is a measure of the difference between the vapour pressures of the solution and the solvent.

9. Lowering of Freezing Point

If the temperature of a solution of a substance in water is lowered ice freezes out, and the temperature at which freezing begins is found to be lower than the freezing point of pure water, 0° C. Raoult has shown that the lowering of the freezing point by a solute is proportional to its molecular concentration. This rule, again, holds only for very dilute solutions.

This law for the lowering of the freezing point can be directly related to the lowering of vapour pressure. If the solid substance separates from a liquid we have an equilibrium between the solid, liquid, and vapour states of the substance. Since liquid and vapour are in equilibrium with each other, and liquid and solid are also in equilibrium, there must obviously be an equilibrium between solid and vapour. The freezing point is thus the temperature at which water and ice have the same vapour pressure. In Fig. 12 a line is drawn to represent

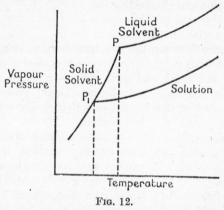

FIG. 12.

the variation of the vapour pressure of water with temperature and another to represent the variation of the vapour pressure of ice with temperature. The point P, where these lines intersect, is the freezing point of water, 0° C.

If we now remember that a solute lowers the vapour pressure of the solvent (see previous paragraph), it is obvious that the line representing the vapour pressure of a solution of sugar in water in Fig. 12 must lie below the curve for pure water. This line cuts the curve representing the vapour pressure of ice at a point P_1, which must, of necessity, be at a lower temperature than P. The lowering of the freezing point is thus a direct consequence of the lowering of vapour pressure.

There is a molecular lowering of the freezing point, Δ, just as there is a molecular elevation of the boiling point. Below are given some values for different solvents. The formula given on p. 18 also holds for the molecular lowering of the freezing point, but Q now stands for the latent heat of fusion of the solvent, and T for the freezing point on the absolute scale.

Below are some values of Δ for a few solvents :

Solvent	Δ	Solvent	Δ
Water . .	18·6°	Phenol . .	74°
Acetic acid .	39°	Benzene . .	49°
Naphthalene .	69°	Camphor . .	400°

The particularly high value for the lowering of the freezing point of camphor is partly due to its high melting point (176°) but predominantly to its small latent heat of fusion (about 5 cals. per gm. ; see the formula on p. 18). Since molten camphor is a good solvent for many organic substances, the lowering of the freezing point of camphor is often used in organic chemistry for the determination of molecular weights (Rast's method).

The lowering of the freezing point is determined in an apparatus due to Beckmann (Fig. 13). The solution under investigation is placed in the tube A, which is separated by an air-jacket from a freezing mixture placed in the beaker C. Stirrers, R_1 and R_2, are placed in A and C, and the temperature at which freezing begins is read off from the Beckmann thermometer. The mercury in the thermometer at first falls steadily and then usually rises slightly, remaining constant for a short time at the freezing point.

We may here consider briefly the question of freezing mixtures. It is well known that if a salt is mixed with ice a mixture is obtained which has a temperature lower than 0° C., the temperature of melting ice. In Beckmann's experiment just described a mixture of ice and potassium nitrate is used as the freezing mixture. Fig. 14 represents the connection between concentration and temperature, and it is seen that either ice or potassium nitrate crystallizes from the solution according to the concentration. Temperatures are plotted as ordinates and concentrations as abscissæ, pure water being represented by the point A, and pure potassium nitrate by the point B. All possible mixtures are thus represented by points between A and B. The point a stands for the freezing point of water. The line aE thus represents the freezing point lowering. The meaning of the line Eb is easy to arrive at if we remember, for example, that the

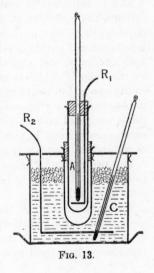

FIG. 13.

solubility of potassium nitrate at 20° is 24·1 per cent., and this is represented by the point c. The line Eb thus gives the compositions of the solutions which are saturated with potassium nitrate, i.e., where solid potassium nitrate is in equilibrium with the solution. At the

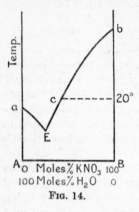

point E we thus have a solution which is in equilibrium not only with ice, but with potassium nitrate also. The point E is called the eutectic point, or the cryohydric point, of the system. If ice and potassium nitrate are brought together some of the ice first melts, and the water produced forms a solution with some of the potassium nitrate, the solution having the composition indicated by the point E. So long as there are potassium nitrate and ice present the temperature remains at the eutectic point, viz., — 3°. Other salts have different eutectic temperatures and thus give freezing mixtures reaching other temperatures. Finally,

FIG. 14.

it should be noted that just as the point a is the melting point of ice, the point b is the melting point of potassium nitrate. The solubility curve of a salt thus extends from the eutectic point E to the melting point of the salt at b (if there are no complications such as hydrate formation, which does not occur in the system dealt with above).

10. Examples of Osmosis in Biology

The transference of water from cell to cell in plants takes place through the operation of osmosis. The plant cell consists essentially of protoplasm and a nucleus more dense than the protoplasm, the whole being enclosed within a cellulose wall. The protoplasm lines the cell wall internally, and a good deal of the volume of the cell is occupied by the vacuole, which is not, as its name might suggest, normally an empty space, but contains cell sap. The cellulose wall is colloidal (see p. 154) and is freely permeable to solvent and solute molecules provided these are small enough to pass between the colloidal particles. All substances present in soil water fall into this class, so that the soil water and its contents can pass freely through the cellulose wall.

The protoplasmic lining, however, is an imperfect semi-permeable membrane. It is freely permeable to water, but also allows certain salts to pass through.

The concentration of the cell sap is normally higher than that of the soil solution. Hence water passes into the cell when it is immersed in soil water, through the protoplasm, and into the vacuole. The cellulose wall is rigid and is incapable of swelling beyond a certain limit (some cell walls are, however, elastic), so there comes a time when no more water can enter unless water is also expelled by the mechanical pressure due to the walls.

This is not the whole story of the intake of water by the plant; the colloidal properties of the cell wall and the cell contents also plays an important part. Water also passes into the plant through the intercellular spaces.

In the actual plant practically the only point of entry of water is the root hairs. Elsewhere, on the stem. leaves, roots, etc., the outside of the cells forming the outer layer of the tissues is covered with a water-resisting cuticle.

If a plant is placed in a solution of which the concentration is greater than that of the cell sap water passes out of the cells by osmosis into the solution. This process is known as exosmosis. The cell contents thus become smaller, the protoplasm breaks away from the cell wall, and indeed the whole vacuole may disappear and the protoplasm gather into a mass within the cell, linked to the walls by only a few strands. When this occurs, plasmolysis is said to have taken place. Some plants, which are specially adapted for living in salt-marshes, have a much more highly concentrated cell sap, which necessarily has a high osmotic pressure. This prevents the too rapid loss of water from the cells and consequent wilting and death of the plant.

The osmotic pressure of the cell sap can be determined by making use of the phenomenon of plasmolysis. Living plant cells are placed in solutions of different known concentrations, and that solution which is just sufficiently concentrated to make the cell show the first signs of plasmolysis is taken as having the same osmotic pressure as the cell contents. This pressure can be calculated from the known law connecting the osmotic pressure of a solution with its concentration. The plasmolytic method was first used by de Vries in 1884. Almost any living plant cells can be used but it is an advantage to use those with coloured sap. The experimental technique is to cut a section of the tissue and observe with a microscope the changes which take place when the section is placed in solutions of different concentrations.

An interesting method of finding the osmotic pressure of cell sap is due to Barger. Drops of sap are sucked into a capillary tube alternately with drops of a solution of known osmotic pressure, say a sugar solution of known concentration. Between each drop there is a bubble of air. The tube is then sealed. After a time either the drops of sap or the drops of solution get larger at the expense of the others. This is due to water molecules leaving the less concentrated solution and passing to the more concentrated, i.e., from the solution of higher vapour pressure to that of lower vapour pressure. As the osmotic pressure of a solution is proportional to the lowering of its vapour pressure (see p. 17), isotonic solutions have the same vapour pressure. The experiment is carried out with a series of tubes, each tube differing from the others in the series by containing a solution of different concentration together with the cell sap. The tube in which no change of size of either the drops of sap or the drops of solution takes place is that in which the solutions are isotonic.

The osmotic pressure of cell sap usually lies between 4 and 5 atmospheres, although the value varies with the nature of the tissue from which the cells are taken. Thus the cambial cells usually contain sap of much higher osmotic pressure, sometimes as high as 25 atmospheres.

Animal cells, unlike plant cells, do not have a rigid cellulose wall. They are enclosed by a protoplasmic membrane which is not rigid but elastic. The entrance of water by osmosis into animal cells causes distension and eventually the cell bursts. This fact is used in Hamburger's method of determining osmotic pressure making use of red blood corpuscles. If water enters these cells they become swollen, and when they burst the red colouring matter, hæmoglobin, passes into the solution, which thereby becomes coloured red. The blood corpuscles are then said to be hæmolysed. If the blood cells are placed in a strong solution of salt or sugar which has a higher osmotic pressure than the contents of the cells, the osmotic flow is in the opposite direction; the cells lose water and become shrivelled or " crenated." They fall to the bottom of the vessel and leave the liquid colourless. By finding the concentration of that solution in which the red blood cells become neither hæmolysed nor crenated, the osmotic pressure of the cell contents can be found, although the results obtained cannot be regarded as entirely satisfactory as the membrane is strong enough to resist rupture for some time, and often hæmolysis only occurs when the osmotic pressure of the external solution is considerably less than isotonic. Mammalian erythrocytes are approximately isotonic with 0·16M sodium chloride.

The osmotic pressure of body fluids is often determined by the method of lowering of freezing point. By this method it has been shown that blood plasma and serum have the same osmotic pressure as the contents of the erythrocytes. This result might have been expected from the shape of the cells; they are biconcave, not biconvex as they would be if the osmotic pressure of the contents were greater than that of the plasma. The osmotic pressure of plasma and tissue fluids is maintained very nearly constant by the taking up of water and the excretion of urine by the animal. The osmotic pressure of urine may vary throughout the day from about 12 to about 24 atmospheres.

In physiological experiments tissues are often examined when they are immersed in " physiological salt solution." The reason for this will now be clear. " Physiological salt solution " is a solution of sodium chloride which has approximately the same osmotic pressure as the contents of the tissue cells under examination, so the cells are not damaged by osmotic effects during the course of the investigation. This solution is sometimes referred to as " normal saline," but it should be remembered that the word *normal* here is not used in the same sense as in volumetric analysis. " Normal saline " is prepared by dissolving 9·5 gm. of sodium chloride in a litre of water. It should be remembered when dealing with cold-blooded animals, that the osmotic pressure of the cell contents is usually less than that of mammals, and consequently the saline used should be less concentrated. 6·5 gm. of sodium chloride dissolved in a litre of water is the common strength used in this case.

11. Summary

In the foregoing paragraphs we have shown that the properties of the solution which we have considered depend upon the number of molecules of the solute which are present in a given volume of the solution.

On the basis of the kinetic theory of gases and the theory of the Brownian movement we have come to the conclusion that the number of independent particles governs the different properties that have been dealt with in this chapter. If any of these properties (known as colligative properties) are used to determine the molecular weight of the substance concerned, it must be borne in mind that a quantity is being determined which is a measure of the number of independent particles of the substance per litre of the solution.

This distinction is emphasized because the results of experiments such as these sometimes give rise to data which are unexpected from ordinary chemical considerations. Suppose, for example, that one sets out to determine the molecular weight of acetic acid from the lowering of the freezing point of water or some other solvent in which the acid is dissolved. One would expect to obtain the value 60 agreeing with the chemical formula CH_3COOH. This expectation is approximately realized if water is the solvent, but if benzene is used a value of about 120 is obtained. The determination of the vapour density of acetic acid vapour also gives a value greater than 60 for the molecular weight. This is because acetic acid associates, partially or completely, to double molecules, both in the vapour state and in solvents such as benzene.

Of course, the molecular weight found from measurements of colligative properties is often that to be expected from the chemical formula of the substance ; but whenever the molecules form larger aggregates, which move independently in the solution, higher values for the molecular weight will be obtained.

As we have repeatedly emphasized, all the foregoing applies only to dilute solutions. The situation with concentrated solutions is much less perfectly understood, and this causes difficulties in dealing with many biological and physico-chemical problems.

12. Suggestions for Further Reading

The theory of dilute solutions is dealt with in all text-books of physical chemistry, and those mentioned in the list on p. 177 might be consulted in this connection.

The subject of osmotic pressure is generally approached from a different angle from that of the present chapter. The reader should try to appreciate how these different approaches may be reconciled with one another.

We would draw attention here to the supplement to this chapter on p. 168, where the membrane equilibrium of colloidal electrolytes is dealt with.

CHAPTER II

REACTION VELOCITY AND EQUILIBRIUM

1. Reaction Velocity in a Homogeneous Medium

MANY reactions of inorganic chemistry take place so rapidly that it is hardly possible to measure their speed. Organic reactions, and reactions taking place in living organisms, however, often occur more slowly, and with measurable speed.

As an example of a reaction of which the speed can be easily determined we may consider the hydrolysis of an ester, such as ethyl acetate, under the influence of a base such as sodium hydroxide :

$$CH_3.COOC_2H_5 + OH^- \rightarrow CH_3.COO^- + C_2H_5OH.$$

This reaction occurs in a homogeneous medium; that is to say, all the reactants and all the products are uniformly distributed in one solution. The reaction in which hydrogen gas and iodine vapour combine to form hydrogen iodide is also a homogeneous reaction since in this case all the substances taking part in the reaction are in the gaseous state. On the other hand, the action of dilute sulphuric acid on zinc is a heterogeneous reaction since one reactant is a liquid and another is a solid, and one of the products is a gas.

If we now consider the reaction velocity of the above-mentioned homogeneous ester hydrolysis further, it is necessary to understand that if an ester molecule is to react with a hydroxyl ion the molecule and the ion must be in each other's immediate neighbourhood. Remembering that all molecules are in motion, we can say that if two molecules are to react with each other it is necessary that they should collide. The number of collisions between the reacting molecules is thus a measure of the speed of the reaction. It is obvious that the number of collisions taking place between unlike molecules in a given time will be doubled if the number of molecules of one kind in a given volume of the reacting system is doubled. Thus, at a given temperature, the number of collisions, and therefore the speed of the reaction, is proportional to the concentration of the reacting substances.

Let us suppose that in our hydrolysis reaction the concentration of the ester is c', and that of the hydroxyl ions is c'', and we consider the decrease in concentration of the ester with time, $-\dfrac{dc'}{dt}$, as a measure of the progress of the reaction. On the basis of the connection between the number of collisions and the concentration deduced above

$$-\frac{dc'}{dt} = kc'c''.$$

If the ester and the hydroxyl ions have the same initial concentrations, $c' = c'' = c$, and we can write

$$-\frac{dc}{dt} = kc^2$$

where k is a constant which is characteristic of this particular reaction. It is called the *velocity constant* of the reaction. If we proceed to integrate this differential equation, we have

$$dt = -\frac{1}{kc^2} \cdot dc = -\frac{1}{k} c^{-2} \, dc$$

$$t = \frac{1}{k} c^{-1} + \text{const.}$$

$$kt = c^{-1} + k \cdot \text{const.}$$

If at times t_1 and t_2, the values of the concentration c are respectively c_1 and c_2, we have

$$kt_2 = c_2^{-1} + k \cdot \text{const.}$$
$$kt_1 = c_1^{-1} + k \cdot \text{const.}$$

Subtracting

$$k(t_2 - t_1) = c_2^{-1} - c_1^{-1} = \frac{c_1 - c_2}{c_1 c_2}$$

$$k = \frac{1}{(t_2 - t_1)} \cdot \frac{c_1 - c_2}{c_1 c_2}.$$

Thus it is possible by determining the concentration at two instants to calculate the velocity constant k.

The above reaction is one in which *two* molecules react with each other, and is therefore called a *bimolecular* reaction. If a reaction involves three reacting molecules it is called a *termolecular* reaction, and by a method analogous to that given above the reaction velocity is given by

$$-\frac{dc'}{dt} = kc'c''c''', \text{ or } -\frac{dc}{dt} = kc^3 \text{ when } c' = c'' = c''' = c.$$

From this it is clear that the velocity of a bimolecular reaction should be proportional to c^2, and that of a termolecular reaction to c^3. Similarly the velocity of a unimolecular reaction should be proportional to c. An example of a unimolecular reaction is that where a substance AB breaks down into A and B, thus

$$AB \rightarrow A + B.$$

If the concentration of AB is c, the velocity of the reaction is given by

$$-\frac{dc}{dt} = kc.$$

If this equation is integrated by a method similar to that used above, we have

$$k = \frac{1}{t_2 - t_1} \log \frac{c_1}{c_2}.$$

As will shortly be seen, the relationship between c and t is not always what would be expected from the equation for the reaction. For this reason, a distinction is often made between the " molecularity " and the " order " of a reaction. The " molecularity " is the number of molecules (or ions) actually concerned in the reaction, or in that step of the reaction which determines the rate ; the " order," on the other hand, is the value of n in the kinetic expression $- \, dc/dt = kc^n$. The " molecularity " and the " order " are often the same, but they may be different.

It is interesting to note how the product of the reciprocal of the initial concentration and the reaction velocity varies from one type of reaction to another. The values of $- \frac{1}{c} . \frac{dc}{dt}$ are given below :

First-order reaction : $- \dfrac{dc}{dt} = kc$, and $- \dfrac{1}{c} . \dfrac{dc}{dt} = k$

Second-order reaction : $- \dfrac{dc}{dt} = kc^2$, and $- \dfrac{1}{c} . \dfrac{dc}{dt} = kc$

Third-order reaction : $- \dfrac{dc}{dt} = kc^3$, and $- \dfrac{1}{c} . \dfrac{dc}{dt} = kc^2$.

By finding experimentally how the concentration of the reactants changes, and then testing the results with the above equations, it is possible to arrive at the equation which holds for the particular reaction. One of the equations would give a constant value for k, and this must be the correct one. From the reaction velocity it is thus possible to deduce the order of the reaction.

For instance, the table below gives experimental data obtained in an investigation of the thermal decomposition of phosphine. It is seen that the expression for a fourth-order reaction, which might be expected to take place from a study of the equation for the reaction

$$4PH_3 \rightarrow P_4 + 6H_2,$$

does not give a constant for k, whereas the expression for a first-order reaction does. The reaction must therefore be represented by the equation

$$PH_3 \rightarrow P + 3H.$$

The reason for this result will be dealt with on p. 34.

Time in hrs.	% decomposition	k according to first-order equation in 10^{-5}/hr.	$k \times C_0{}^3$ according to fourth-order equation 10^{-5}/hr. C_0-initial concn.
0	0	—	—
7·83	4·17	544	580
24·17	12·37	546	670
41·25	19·97	540	769
63·17	29·29	549	965
89·67	39·23	555	1285

In some cases the formula for the reaction velocity is of a simpler type than would be expected from a consideration of the chemical equation ; this, indeed, is the case for the decomposition of phosphine referred to above. The inversion of cane sugar provides another example. This reaction takes place according to the equation

$$C_{12}H_{22}O_{11} + H_2O \rightarrow \underset{\text{glucose}}{C_6H_{12}O_6} + \underset{\text{fructose}}{C_6H_{12}O_6}$$

and there is no doubt that the reaction is bimolecular in the sense that it involves a series of collisions between one sugar molecule and one water molecule. It would therefore be expected to show second-order kinetics, but in fact a first-order rate law is followed. It must be remembered that the reaction is studied when the sugar is dissolved in water. In consequence the concentration of the water is incomparably greater than that of the sugar. The number of water molecules present at the beginning of the experiment is thus little more than at the end, and therefore the concentration of the water may be regarded as a constant, and the reaction is to all intents and purposes a reaction of the first order. Suppose we take a 1 per cent. solution of cane sugar, i.e., 10 gm. of cane sugar in 990 gm. of water. The molecular weight of cane sugar is 342, that of water is 18. The mixture thus consists of $\frac{10}{342}$, i.e., approximately $\frac{1}{34}$ gm.-mol. of sugar in $\frac{990}{18} = 55$ gm.-mol. of water. At the end of the reaction the number of water molecules has decreased from 55 to $54\frac{33}{34}$, i.e., by 0·06 per cent., whereas the sugar concentration has decreased by 100 per cent. It is therefore quite legitimate to assume that the concentration of the water remains constant.

This reaction is followed very satisfactorily by means of the polarimeter, as the original cane sugar rotates the plane of polarization of light to a different extent from the invert sugar formed. If the rotation of the plane of polarization for the pure cane sugar solution is $a°$ and that for the completely inverted sugar is $-\beta°$, then the rotation when $(100 - x)$ per cent. is inverted and x per cent. of cane sugar remains is

$$-\frac{(100 - x)}{100}\,\beta + \frac{x}{100}\,a = -\beta + \frac{(a + \beta)}{100}\,x.$$

If this angle of rotation is given the symbol γ, x, the percentage of cane sugar remaining, can be calculated from γ as follows :

$$\gamma = -\beta + \frac{(a + \beta)}{100}\,x \text{ or } \frac{x}{100} = \frac{\gamma + \beta}{a + \beta}.$$

The following table shows that the experimental results agree satisfactorily with the first-order equation. The constant k is calculated from the equation

$$k = \frac{1}{t} \log \frac{100}{x} = \frac{1}{t \times 0\cdot 4343} \log_{10}\left(\frac{25\cdot 16 + 8\cdot 3}{\gamma + 8\cdot 3}\right),$$

since a for pure cane sugar is $25\cdot 16°$ and β for invert sugar is $-8\cdot 3°$.

Time in mins.	Angle of rotation, γ	k (min $^{-1}$)
0	25·16	—
56	16·95	503×10^{-5}
116	10·38	503
176	5·46	505
236	1·85	506
371	− 3·28	511
∞	− 8·3	
	mean k	$506 \times 10^{-5}\,\text{min}^{-1}$

2. Catalysis

The reaction dealt with above proceeds extremely slowly by itself. As is well known the addition of a small amount of an acid accelerates the reaction to a great extent. The actual substance responsible for the acceleration of the reaction has been proved to be the hydrogen ion which is split off by all acids (see p. 62).

A substance which accelerates (or decelerates) a reaction is called a catalyst. The catalyst must remain unchanged at the end of the reaction.

We may distinguish between homogeneous and heterogeneous catalysis according as whether the catalyst mixes homogeneously with the reactants or not. The above-mentioned example—the catalysis of the inversion of cane sugar by acids—is an example of homogeneous catalysis. The combination of hydrogen and oxygen catalysed by spongy platinum is an example of heterogeneous catalysis. We have mentioned already that there are also catalysts which slow down a reaction. They are called negative catalysts. The reaction

$$2Na_2SO_3 + O_2 \rightarrow 2Na_2SO_4,$$

for example, is strongly inhibited by the addition of organic substances such as mannitol, aniline, benzaldehyde, etc. These substances are negative catalysts for this reaction.

It is evident that the accelerating effect of a catalyst could be proportional to its concentration, c'. If we think of the accelerating effect of a catalyst as characterized by a factor, k', then the speed of the reaction will be increased by the catalyst proportionally to c' and to c, k' being the proportionality factor.

Thus, for a first-order reaction :

$$-\frac{dc}{dt} = kc + k'c'c = c(k + k'c')$$

and thus the catalysed and non-catalysed reactions take place independently, side by side.

For a given quantity of catalyst added, the magnitude $(k + k'c')$ is a constant, and may be written k_k. The last equation may then be written

$$-\frac{dc}{dt} = k_k c.$$

This equation is again that governing a first-order reaction, but the velocity constant has a different value from that which it would have had if there had been no catalyst present. Negative catalysis cannot be explained as two reactions running side by side. In cases of negative catalysis it has to be assumed that the catalyst interferes in the mechanism of the uncatalysed reaction, e.g. by taking away an intermediate product of the reaction.

3. Autocatalysis

It sometimes happens that during the course of a reaction a product is formed which itself accelerates or decelerates the reaction; or, in other words, that one of the reaction products acts as a catalyst. This catalytic effect becomes more and more marked in proportion as the quantity of catalyst formed becomes greater, so that the reaction proceeds more rapidly (or more slowly if a negative catalyst is formed) as time goes on. As an example we may take the well-known oxidimetric titration of oxalic acid with potassium permanganate, which is accelerated by the manganous sulphate formed :

$$2KMnO_4 + 5C_2H_2O_4 + 3H_2SO_4 \rightarrow K_2SO_4 + 2MnSO_4 + 10CO_2 + 8H_2O.$$

The reaction, which is very slow initially, gradually proceeds faster and faster as more of the catalyst, manganous sulphate, is formed.

Let the initial concentration of a reactant in a first-order reaction be c, and suppose that at a given time t a quantity x of the reaction product is formed. The concentration of the reactant is now $c - x$. We thus get an equation for the reaction velocity similar in form to that obtained in the preceding paragraph, but now the concentration of the catalyst is represented by x. Thus,

$$-\frac{d(c - x)}{dt} = k(c - x) + k'(c - x)x = (k + k'x)\,(c - x).$$

As an example of negative autocatalysis we may mention the esterification of an organic acid (in this case phenylacetic acid) with alcohol, which occurs under the influence of added hydrogen ions. The equation is

$$C_6H_5CH_2COOH + C_2H_5OH \rightarrow C_6H_5CH_2COOC_2H_5 + H_2O.$$

The phenylacetic acid itself will, of course, give rise to hydrogen ions which catalyse the reaction, but during the course of the reaction they gradually disappear; so negative autocatalysis is occurring.

4. Complex Reactions

It has been mentioned that the final product of a reaction might not be formed by a single reaction from the initial reactants, but that we might have to deal with a series of reactions. These complex reactions can be divided into a number of groups. Thus :

Simultaneous reactions. Take, for example, the reaction involved in the nitration of benzoic acid. *Ortho-*, *meta-*, and *para*-nitrobenzoic acids are formed. We have here three reactions proceeding together. It is obvious that the decrease in the concentration of the benzoic acid will be given by the sum of the decreases brought about by each of these reactions. If the total velocity of reaction is given by $-\dfrac{dc}{dt}$ and the velocities of the individual reactions are $\dfrac{dx}{dt}$, $\dfrac{dy}{dt}$, and $\dfrac{dz}{dt}$, then

$$-\frac{dc}{dt} = \frac{dx}{dt} + \frac{dy}{dt} + \frac{dz}{dt} = k_1 c + k_2 c + k_3 c = (k_1 + k_2 + k_3)c = kc.$$

Hence, the velocity constant, k, of the total reaction is the sum of the constants k_1, k_2, and k_3, of the three individual reactions.

Consecutive reactions. If we have a reaction which can be represented as follows :

$$A + B \rightarrow C + D \rightarrow E + F$$

in which the products of the first reaction react again in a new way giving different reaction products, the series is called a set of consecutive reactions. The velocity with which the final product is formed will obviously be determined by the slowest reaction of the series. If, therefore, the reaction velocity of a number of consecutive reactions is measured it is always only the velocity of the slowest of the reactions that is actually determined. This means that it is quite possible for the results of determinations of reaction velocities to lead sometimes to unexpected conclusions. The investigation of the reaction velocity of the thermal decomposition of phosphine, mentioned above, leads to the conclusion that it is a first-order reaction following the equation :

$$PH_3 \rightarrow P + 3H.$$

As, of course, phosphorus vapour has four atoms to the molecule, and hydrogen two, the equation should be

$$4PH_3 \rightarrow P_4 + 6H_2.$$

Nevertheless, experiment shows that the reaction proceeds according to a first-order rate law (see p. 29). Clearly we are concerned here with these consecutive reactions :

$$PH_3 \rightarrow P + 3H, \quad 4P \rightarrow P_4, \quad 2H \rightarrow H_2,$$

and the predominant velocity is that of the first reaction, because this is the slowest, the two others proceeding practically instantaneously.

If the decrease in concentration of one of the original reactants with time is determined, say, $-\dfrac{dc_A}{dt}$, then it is only the reaction velocity of the first part of the series that is being measured.

Chain reactions. A chain reaction is a special type of consecutive reaction in which reaction chains comprising many thousands of links can be formed. A typical chain reaction is that between hydrogen and chlorine. A mixture of these two gases reacts only very slowly at ordinary temperature in the dark. The reaction becomes, however, very much more rapid if a chlorine molecule in the mixture is broken up into chlorine atoms. This can be done by exposing the mixture to light, by heating, or by the introduction of some sodium :

$$\overset{\text{light or heat}}{Cl_2 \rightarrow 2Cl}$$
$$Cl_2 + Na \rightarrow NaCl + Cl$$

A chlorine atom thus formed now reacts with a hydrogen molecule leaving a free hydrogen atom, which in its turn reacts with a chlorine molecule liberating a chlorine atom, and the whole process is repeated.

$$Cl + H_2 \rightarrow HCl + H$$
$$H + Cl_2 \rightarrow HCl + Cl, \text{ and so on.}$$

In this case the reaction chain may become many millions of links long. The chain may be broken if the free atoms unite by any of the following reactions :

$$Cl + Cl \rightarrow Cl_2$$
$$Cl + H \rightarrow HCl$$
$$H + H \rightarrow H_2$$

Because of the small concentrations of the free atoms, however, these stopping reactions very seldom take place.

In this chain reaction one free atom (or free radical) gives rise to the formation of thousands of molecules. In another type of chain reaction all the reaction products link up to form a very large molecule.

Styrene, $C_6H_5CH : CH_2$, has a double bond which, under the influence of light or heat breaks down into a single bond, the two neighbouring carbon atoms then possessing a free valency :

$$C_6H_5.CH : CH_2 \rightarrow C_6H_5.CH.CH_2$$

When this molecule with the free valencies comes into contact with a normal molecule one of the free valencies is satisfied by attaching itself to the other molecule, but free valencies are formed at the ends of the molecule thus :

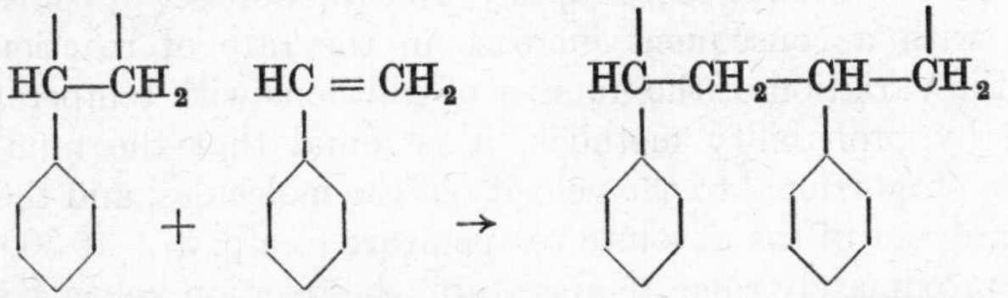

The double molecule formed is just as reactive as the original molecule which possessed free valencies, and reacts with another styrene molecule, and eventually a very long chain molecule is formed, called polystyrene. This contains many thousands of styrene molecules linked together. The remarkable properties of these macromolecules will be dealt with in Chapter IX.

Opposing reactions. It is possible for a reaction to give rise to products which can recombine to form the original substance ; for example :

ester + water = acid + alcohol
acid + alcohol = ester + water.

This phenomenon gives rise to such important conclusions that it will be dealt with more generally later (see p. 43).

We have dealt briefly with these more complicated cases in order to give the student an idea of how necessary it is to proceed carefully in drawing conclusions from the results of velocity determinations.

5. Effect of the Medium

It often happens that a reaction takes one course in a certain medium and a different one in another, but the order of the reaction in both media is the same. The velocity constants, however, are different.

Thus, for example, the velocity of isomerization of ammonium cyanate :

$$\underset{\text{ammonium cyanate}}{NH_4CNO} \rightarrow \underset{\text{urea}}{NH_2 . CO . NH_2}$$

is thirty times as great if the ammonium cyanate is dissolved in alcohol as when it is dissolved in water.

This difference cannot, of course, be ascribed to a difference in the number of collisions, so that there must be some other factors which influence the reaction velocity. We shall return to this point in the next section. Neutral salts often exert a well-marked effect on reaction velocity ; for example, in the inversion of cane sugar (in the presence of acids) and in the hydrolysis of esters.

6. Effect of Temperature

Temperature has a very great effect on the velocity of a reaction. It is tempting to explain this fact as follows : if the temperature is raised the particles move more rapidly, and the number of collisions is increased, with a consequent increase in the rate of reaction. If, however, the variation of the number of collisions with temperature is calculated by probability methods, it is found that the number of collisions is proportional to the velocity of the molecules, and therefore to the square root of the absolute temperature (see p. 3) ; at 300° Abs. (i.e., at approximately room temperature) the reaction velocity should be about one-sixth per cent. per degree greater in consequence of the increased number of collisions. Experiment, however, leads to quite a different result. Reaction velocities may increase by as much as 100 to 300 per cent. or more for a 10° rise of temperature.

Many years ago Arrhenius put forward the following equation for the effect of temperature on the velocity constant, k :

$$k = Ze^{-A/T} = Ze^{-E/RT}$$

As RT has the dimensions of energy, E also represents an energy. In order to understand the meaning of this energy E, we consider a reaction

$$XY + Z \rightarrow X + YZ$$

Now we know that the rate of the reaction is dependent upon the number of collisions of the molecules XY and Z in a given time. Calculation shows that not all collisions can lead to combination. If all collisions were effective reaction velocities would be, in general, much greater than they actually are. Not all collisions, then, are effective, the explanation being that a certain minimum amount of energy must be possessed by the colliding molecules before reaction can occur. This minimum amount of energy is called the activation energy, and its nature may be made clear by a simple example. Suppose we consider a stone lying in a roof-gutter (Fig. 15). If the stone were to fall to the ground a quantity of energy represented by the vertical distance A would be given out (mainly as heat). But before the stone could fall it would have to be lifted to the edge of the gutter, and energy B would have to be supplied for this purpose. B may be termed the activation energy for the whole process.

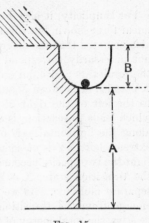

FIG. 15.

Let us now consider the reaction of XY with Z to give the products X and YZ. (X, Y, and Z might be either atoms or groups of atoms.) When XY approaches Z, work has to be done against the repulsive forces between them, and the potential energy of the system thus increases. In Fig. 16 this potential energy is plotted against the distance between XY and Z, as is also the potential energy for the system X and YZ, against the distance between X and YZ. The position T on the diagram represents the so-called "transition state" for the reaction, when the bond between X and Y has been partly

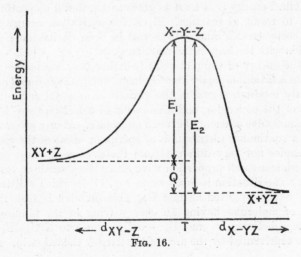

FIG. 16.

broken and the bond between Y and Z partly made. On this view, the course of the reaction may be represented :

$$XY + Z \rightarrow X \text{-}\text{-} Y \text{-}\text{-} Z \rightarrow X + YZ.$$

For simplicity, it may be assumed that the transition state has the linear form shown, but this is not necessary to the argument. It should also be noted that the diagram is not exact, in that the position T does not necessarily correspond to zero distance between the reactants or the resultants ; also, an ordinary collision (without reaction) between XY and Z or between X and YZ will be represented by a point a little to the left or the right of T. Thus, a collision between XY and Z which leads to reaction, is described by the motion of a point moving along the horizontal axis of the diagram from left to right. At the extreme left, XY is at some distance from Z, but as we move to the right the two species become closer together, until at T we have reached the transition state, X - - Y - - Z, and XY has lost its identity as a separate molecule. As we now proceed to the right, X and YZ emerge from the transition state and move further apart. As can be seen, the total energy of the system increases as the molecules come nearer together, and is a maximum for the transition state. Conversely, for XY and Z to come within a specified distance of each other, they must together possess enough energy to overcome the repulsive forces between them up to this distance, and this necessary energy is, of course, that shown on the diagram. Thus, if the combined energy of XY and Z is less than E_1, they will not be able to attain the transition state, reaction will be impossible, and they will simply collide while retaining their separate identities. If, on the other hand, the combined energy is at least as great as E_1, it will be possible for a collision to result in reaction. E_1 is the activation energy for the reaction between XY and Z ; as can be seen, it has no necessary connection with the heat of the reaction Q.

Now the energy of the molecules (whether they are in the gaseous state or in solution) is partly kinetic, due to their translational motions, and partly internal, stored in the various vibrational and rotational motions of the molecules, and as a result of collisions there is a continual interchange of energy between molecules. At any given instant, there is a continuous distribution of energies ; most of the molecules have energies not very different from the average or most probable energy, while a small proportion have either very small or very large energies. The situation is as shown in Fig. 17, in which a distribution function $N(U)$ is plotted against U. This function is such that the number of molecules having an energy lying in the infinitesimally small range between U_1 and $U_1 + dU$ is equal to $N(U_1)dU$, and is therefore represented by the area of the narrow shaded strip. From a distribution curve of this kind, it is possible to calculate the proportion of molecular collisions in which the total energy is greater than a specified amount E, and for fairly simple molecules this proportion is found to be $e^{-E/RT}$ where e is the base of natural logarithms. It is readily shown that this expression increases very rapidly, (a) as E decreases, (b) as T increases. This may be seen qualitatively from Fig. 17, on which the number of molecules having energy greater than E is represented by the shaded area C. If, now, the ordinate ab is moved slightly to the left, corresponding to a small decrease in E, the area C increases considerably, because of the steepness of the distribution curve in this region. On the other hand, an increase in temperature

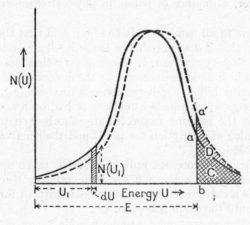

FIG. 17.

means an increase in the average energy of the molecules and a new distribution curve—the dotted curve. The number of molecules with energy greater than E is now represented by the shaded area D. It is this large effect on the factor $e^{-E/RT}$ which produces the large effect of temperature on the velocity of chemical reactions. Not all collisions with energy in excess of E_1 will lead to reaction—XY and Z may have enough energy to reach the transition state, but may once again emerge from it without reacting—but we can assume that a certain fixed fraction will do so. Indeed, in a simplified treatment such as the present one, we can assume that both this fraction and the collision frequency (the number of collisions per second) are independent of temperature. We can then write for the rate of reaction between XY and Z

$$k_1 = A_1 e^{-E_1/RT} \text{ or } \log k_1 = \log A_1 - E_1/RT$$

This is in fact the Arrhenius equation mentioned on p. 36.

In the case of a true unimolecular decomposition, the decomposing molecules must similarly gain an amount of energy at least equal to an activation energy before they can react. This energy is gained by molecular collisions, so that collisions play an essential part in determining the rate of a unimolecular reaction, even although only one molecule is concerned in each actual decomposition process.

To discuss what precisely is the nature of the activated state would take us beyond the scope of this book. Suffice it to say that it is connected with the displacement of electrons in the atoms which make up the molecule. If we accept the possibility of an activated state, however, a number of points in physical chemistry are made clear.

There is first of all catalysis. It has been said that the catalyst is not used up ; that it does not change the order of a reaction, but only increases the velocity constant, k. Its function is thus clearly to reduce the obstacle which must be overcome by the molecules before they can react (the energy hill). For heterogeneous catalysis (e.g., the use of platinum sponge which causes a mixture of hydrogen and oxygen to react rapidly) the reacting molecules are adsorbed on the platinum (for the meaning of adsorption see p. 91) and their activation energy is thus decreased.

In photochemical processes, radiant energy is taken up in order to supply the energy of activation for some primary reaction, which often initiates a chain reaction which proceeds without further activation energy until the chain is broken.

The activation energy may assume a wide range of values, but $E = 20,000$ cals/mole can be considered as representative. Comparing velocity constants at $10°$ intervals one obtains

$$\frac{k_{T+10}}{k_T} = \frac{Ze^{-R/E\,(T+10)}}{Ze^{-E/RT}} = e^{\frac{10\,E}{RT\,(T+10)}}$$

where we assumed the collision number Z to be independent of the temperature.

The quotient $k_{T+10}\,k_T$ is often written Q_{10}, particularly in biological literature. Q_{10} thus depends on T and on the activation energy E, which is characteristic for each reaction.

With $E = 20,000$ cals/mole, $R = 2$ cals/mole and $T = 300°$ ($= 27°$ C.), $10\,E/RT(T+10)$ is close to unity and consequently $Q_{10} \approx 2\cdot7$.

Some values of Q_{10} are given in the table below.

Reaction	Temp.	Q_{10}
$H_2 + I_2 \rightarrow 2HI$	445° C.	1·47
$2HI \rightarrow H_2 + I_2$	445° C.	1·53
$PH_3 \rightarrow P + 3H$	720° C.	1·8
$CH_3COOC_2H_5 + NaOH \rightarrow CH_3COONa + C_2H_5OH$.	25° C.	1·9
$KClO_3 + 6FeSO_4 + 3H_2SO_4 \rightarrow KCl + 3Fe_2(SO_4)_3 + 3H_2O$.	20° C.	2·44
$CH_2ClCOOH + H_2O \rightarrow CH_2OHCOOH + HCl$.	100° C.	2·55
Inversion of cane sugar	40° C.	3·63

We may now deal briefly with what is called " false equilibrium"·
It often happens that the velocity of a reaction is so small that even
after a very long time it is impossible to detect the slightest change in
the system. For example, all organic substances oxidize on exposure
to air, and this reaction may be made to go faster if the temperature is
raised. It is therefore to some extent reasonable to assume that the
oxidation reaction will take place at low temperatures, but with an
infinitesimally small velocity. The oxidation of hydrogen to form
water has been fully studied from this point of view, and it has been
shown that this reaction, which proceeds violently at high temperatures (above 700°), takes place more and more slowly as the
temperature is reduced, until at temperatures below 400° the rate of
reaction is so slow that it practically defies observation. Yet the
system $H_2 + O_2$ is not in equilibrium at the lower temperatures, and
the reaction does go on. This state of affairs where no apparent
change takes place is wrongly called " false equilibrium", or, better,
" apparent equilibrium". It is obvious that a catalyst can alter this
state of false equilibrium.

7. Reaction Velocity in a Heterogeneous System

The reactions with which we have dealt so far proceed in a homogeneous liquid or gaseous phase.

If, however, it is desired to investigate, for example, the velocity
with which magnesium oxide is attacked by hydrochloric acid, the
reaction to be studied is heterogeneous :

$$MgO + 2HCl \rightarrow MgCl_2 + H_2O.$$

This is because magnesium oxide is a
solid, and the other participants are, of
course, dissolved, and in the liquid state.

Suppose we consider a block of
magnesium oxide which is placed in
dilute hydrochloric acid, of concentration c (Fig. 18). Reaction can only
take place at the surface of the magnesium oxide, where the latter comes

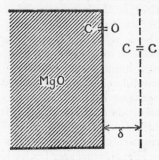

FIG. 18.

into contact with the hydrochloric acid. The actual reaction between the magnesium oxide and the hydrochloric acid is extremely fast, so that the concentration of the hydrochloric acid adjacent to the magnesium oxide surface soon approaches zero. The hydrochloric acid thereupon starts to diffuse from the bulk of the solution to the layer near the oxide, and the observed speed of the reaction is obviously dependent upon this speed of diffusion. If the liquid is stirred vigorously the diffusion now has to take place only through a thin layer of liquid that clings to the magnesium oxide surface, and so the reaction is greatly accelerated.

Fick's law (p. 10) gives the weight dm of a substance diffusing in time dt as :

$$dm = - Dq \frac{dc}{dx} dt.$$

Here D is the diffusion coefficient, q the small area across which diffusion takes place, and dc/dx the concentration gradient, which is assumed to be constant over the whole of the area q. If we assume that the thickness of the thin surface layer of solution mentioned above is δ, and that the concentration of acid changes uniformly from c (its value in the bulk of the solution) to zero, across this surface layer, then the concentration gradient dc/dx is simply c/δ. If, further, the total surface area of the magnesium oxide is O, the volume of the solution V, and the total weight of acid diffusing in time dt is dM, we have :

$$\frac{dM}{dt} = - DO \frac{c}{\delta}$$

or

$$\frac{1}{V} \cdot \frac{dM}{dt} = - \left[\frac{DO}{\delta V} \right] c$$

i.e.,

$$\frac{dc}{dt} = - \left[\frac{DO}{\delta V} \right] c$$

Since the quantity in brackets will be constant in a given situation, the rate of consumption of acid will follow the first-order rate law as is, in fact, found to be the case. As Nernst and Brunner have verified the above relationship experimentally, it may be concluded that the velocity of reaction in a heterogeneous system shows the characteristics of a unimolecular reaction. Conversely, it is clear that one must be careful about concluding that because a reaction follows the first-order equation it is necessarily a unimolecular reaction. It is necessary to ascertain that the reaction is taking place in a homogeneous medium before deciding, for, as has been shown above, every heterogeneous reaction under the conditions described follows the first-order law.

Hinshelwood and Topley have clearly demonstrated that the thermal decomposition of phosphine dealt with on p. 29 is not a homogeneous unimolecular gas reaction, but takes place on the walls of the reaction vessel and is therefore a heterogeneous reaction. We are therefore here concerned with heterogeneous catalysis. In the case of heterogeneous catalysis, which plays such an important part not only in industrial processes, but also in biological processes (e.g. enzyme systems), diffusion near the catalysing surface is the rate-determining factor.

8. Equilibrium Phenomena

If the reaction

$$A + B \rightleftharpoons C + D$$

taking place in a homogeneous system, is of such a type that A and B react together to give C and D, but conversely C and D react together to re-form A and B, we have to deal with two *opposing reactions* (see p. 35). As an example we may take

$$\text{alcohol} + \text{acid} \rightleftharpoons \text{ester} + \text{water}.$$

For the reaction between A and B we have

$$-\frac{dc_1}{dt} = k_1 C_A C_B.$$

For the reaction between C and D

$$-\frac{dc_2}{dt} = k_2 C_C C_D.$$

These equations are statements of Guldberg and Waage's Law of Mass Action, which states that the rate of a chemical reaction is proportional to the product of the active masses of the reactants. The active masses are generally taken as equal to the molecular concentrations in a homogeneous system. For heterogeneous reactions, however, we shall see that the active masses of some reactants are properly taken as constant.

Since the reactions are opposing it is obvious that there will be a state when the two velocities $-\frac{dc_1}{dt}$ and $-\frac{dc_2}{dt}$ are equal, and this will be the case when the same number of molecules of A and B react to give C and D, as C and D molecules react to give A and B. We thus have a state of dynamic equilibrium.

$$-\frac{dc_1}{dt} = -\frac{dc_2}{dt}$$

Then

$$k_1 C_A C_B = k_2 C_C C_D$$

so that in the state of equilibrium

$$\frac{C_C C_D}{C_A C_B} = \frac{k_1}{k_2} = K$$

where k_1 and k_2 are the velocity constants, and their ratio, K, is the *equilibrium constant*.

Let us consider such a reaction as ester formation and ester hydrolysis further. Whichever of the two possibilities is taken as the starting point, either alcohol + acid, or ester + water, the reaction goes on until the reaction products are in equilibrium with the reactants. The relationship deduced above must hold, and we can write

$$\frac{C_{\text{ester}} \times C_{\text{water}}}{C_{\text{alcohol}} \times C_{\text{acid}}} = K.$$

The experimental investigation of this reaction shows that the state of equilibrium is reached at room temperature when the reaction starting from alcohol + acid has proceeded until about two-thirds of the reactants is converted. If we assume that the concentrations of the reactants are equal, and are represented by C, then at equilibrium we have

$$K = \frac{\frac{2}{3}C \times \frac{2}{3}C}{\frac{1}{3}C \times \frac{1}{3}C} = 4.$$

We thus see that the equilibrium constant for the esterification reaction is 4, and we can say that if other concentrations of the reactants had been chosen the relationship for the equilibrium must always hold, so that the equilibrium constant is always 4.

This leads us to the following point: If, now, the concentration of one of the reactants—e.g., C_A—is increased, then C_B must decrease and C_C and C_D increase, in order that K should remain constant. In other words, if a system in equilibrium is disturbed by the addition of more of one of the reactants, a new position of equilibrium is reached which corresponds to the further reaction of the added reactant. Conversely, removal of one of the reactants causes more of that reactant to be produced. In less exact language, addition of excess of any of the reactants " shifts the equilibrium over towards the other side."

If in a reaction more than one molecule of one of the substances takes part, the above expression takes a somewhat different form. Let us consider the case where one molecule splits up into two, e.g.,

$$A \rightleftharpoons 2B.$$

The expression for the velocity of the reaction from left to right is now

$$-\frac{dc}{dt} = k_1 C_A,$$

and from right to left

$$-\frac{dc}{dt} = k_2 C_B^2.$$

$$K = \frac{C_B^2}{C_A}.$$

In the general case the equation for the equilibrium for a reaction of the type

$$m\text{A} + n\text{B} + p\text{C} \rightleftharpoons q\text{D} + r\text{E}$$

is
$$K = \frac{C_D{}^q C_E{}^r}{C_A{}^m C_B{}^n C_C{}^p} \quad \text{or} \quad \frac{[\text{D}]^q [\text{E}]^r}{[\text{A}]^m [\text{B}]^n [\text{C}]^p},$$

where the quantities in square brackets represent the molecular concentration (i.e., the number of gram-molecules per litre) of the substance concerned. Thus, for the equilibrium constant of the reaction $N_2O_4 \rightleftharpoons 2NO_2$ we have

$$\frac{[\text{NO}_2]^2}{[\text{N}_2\text{O}_4]} = K$$

and for the dissociation of hydrogen iodide, $2\text{HI} \rightleftharpoons \text{H}_2 + \text{I}_2$,

$$\frac{[\text{H}_2][\text{I}_2]}{[\text{HI}]^2} = K.$$

In the decomposition of phosphine (§ 1 and § 4 of this chapter) we have a reaction of which the kinetics follow a different equation (viz., the first-order equation) from that which one would expect on the basis of the stoichiometrical equation. This has no effect, however, on the law of mass action. The equilibrium equations can be correctly written down only when the stoichiometry of the reaction is known.

In the case of the decomposition of phosphine this can be shown as follows. We have here three reactions which, at equilibrium, are each in equilibrium with the other :

$$\text{PH}_3 \rightleftharpoons \text{P} + 3\text{H}$$
$$4\text{P} \rightleftharpoons \text{P}_4$$
$$2\text{H} \rightleftharpoons \text{H}_2$$

If the equilibrium constants of these reactions are K_1, K_2, and K_3, we have

$$K_1 = \frac{[\text{P}][\text{H}]^3}{[\text{PH}_3]}$$

$$K_2 = \frac{[\text{P}_4]}{[\text{P}]^4}$$

$$K_3 = \frac{[\text{H}_2]}{[\text{H}]^2}$$

The concentrations of the hydrogen atoms and the phosphorus atoms can be eliminated from these equations when we have

$$\frac{[\text{P}_4][\text{H}_2]^6}{[\text{PH}_3]^4} = K_1{}^4 . K_2 . K_3{}^6 = K$$

This is the same conclusion which would have been reached had we tarted with the reaction equation

$$4\text{PH}_3 \rightleftharpoons \text{P}_4 + 6\text{H}_2$$

Experiment shows that a catalyst changes the speed of a reaction but not the concentrations of the substances present at equilibrium. The equilibrium constant K is thus independent of any added catalyst. As this constant K is the quotient of the two velocity constants, k_1 and k_2, the catalyst must affect the two opposing reactions to exactly the same extent.

The foregoing discussion applies, as has already been emphasized, only to a homogeneous system. It has, however, been shown that the above considerations can also apply to a heterogeneous equilibrium if the reasoning is modified accordingly. We will consider first the vapour of ammonium chloride in equilibrium with ammonia and hydrogen chloride :

$$NH_4Cl \rightleftharpoons NH_3 + HCl.$$

According to the law of mass action we have

$$\frac{[NH_3]\,[HCl]}{[NH_4Cl]} = K$$

so long as all the reactants and products are in the gaseous state. Suppose now that solid ammonium chloride is deposited from the vapour. In the vapour phase, of course, the law holds ; the deposited ammonium chloride will have a certain vapour pressure at the temperature of the experiment, which thus gives rise to a certain concentration $[NH_4Cl]$. This concentration remains the same throughout the experiment so long as the vapour exists in the presence of solid ammonium chloride. We can incorporate this constant concentration in the expression for the equilibrium constant, and we can say that for ammonium chloride vapour in equilibrium with solid ammonium chloride

$$[NH_3]\,[HCl] = K[NH_4Cl] = K'$$

is true. In fact, it is doubtful whether ammonium chloride exists in the vapour state ; probably the solid ammonium chloride decomposes directly to gaseous ammonia and hydrogen chloride. Now the rate of this decomposition will depend solely on the temperature, while the rate of the re-combination reaction at a given temperature will be proportional to the product of the concentrations of gaseous ammonia and hydrogen chloride. For equilibrium, the rate of decomposition must be equal to the rate of re-combination, and it will readily be seen that this gives the expression for K' which has been deduced above on more doubtful grounds. Similar reasoning applies to other cases of heterogeneous equilibrium, and leads to the general conclusion that the "active masses " of solids in an equilibrium involving gases or liquids must be taken as constant.

For the reaction
$$CaCO_3 \rightleftharpoons CaO + CO_2$$
which occurs in the lime kiln, two of the concentrations are constant, viz., those of the calcium carbonate and the calcium oxide. The law of mass action thus leads to the simple equation
$$p_{CO2} = \text{constant},$$
which indicates that the pressure of the carbon dioxide is independent of the quantities of solid calcium oxide and solid calcium carbonate present (provided that both are there) and depends only on the temperature.

9. Effect of Pressure and Temperature on the Equilibrium. Dynamic Equilibrium

(a) *Effect of pressure.* Consider the reaction that has already been used as an example above,
$$N_2O_4 \rightleftharpoons 2NO_2.$$
Let us suppose that we have a gaseous mixture of these oxides of nitrogen at a pressure P, and that the partial pressure of N_2O_4 is p_1 and that of NO_2 is p_2. Then $P = p_1 + p_2$.

Since
$$\frac{[NO_2]^2}{[N_2O_4]} = K$$

$$\frac{p_2^2}{p_1} = K \quad . \quad . \quad . \quad . \quad . \quad . \quad . \quad . \quad (1)$$

Let us suppose that the gas mixture is compressed to half its original volume. By the simple application of Boyle's law we arrive at the conclusion that the total pressure is now $2P$ and the partial pressures $2p_1$ and $2p_2$. The law of mass action would now give

$$K = \frac{4p_2^2}{2p_1} = \frac{2p_2^2}{p_1} \quad . \quad . \quad . \quad . \quad . \quad . \quad (2)$$

It is clear, however, that the K in equation (1) and that in equation (2) are not the same, but the second is twice as great as the first. If the law of mass action is to be correct at the smaller volume it is obvious that the numerator in the last equation must become smaller, and the denominator greater. In other words a number of NO_2 molecules must combine with each other to give N_2O_4 molecules in consequence of the increased pressure.

Let us now consider another example, the thermal decomposition of hydrogen iodide.
$$2HI \rightleftharpoons H_2 + I_2$$
$$p_1 \qquad p_2 \quad p_3$$
(the symbols below the formulæ stand for the partial pressures of the molecular species above them).

In this case the law of mass action gives

$$\frac{p_2 p_3}{p_1^2} = K \quad . \quad . \quad . \quad . \quad . \quad . \quad . \quad . \quad . \quad (3)$$

If the total pressure, P, which is equal to the sum of the partial pressures, is doubled, we can write

$$\frac{4p_2 p_3}{4p_1^2} = K,$$

remembering that the partial pressures are also doubled. Dividing both numerator and denominator by 4 we have the same equation as (3). We thus see that in the case of the thermal decomposition of hydrogen iodide change of pressure exerts no influence on the equilibrium.

Comparing the two examples more closely, it is seen that alteration of pressure only exerts an effect on the equilibrium if the reaction is one that takes place with change of volume. In the gaseous state the volume is proportional to the number of molecules (Avogadro's hypothesis). We can therefore tell whether there will be a change of volume when a reaction takes place by seeing if there is any difference in the number of molecules on the left- and right-hand sides of the equation. In the dissociation of nitrogen tetroxide, N_2O_4, there is one molecule on the left-hand side of the equation and two on the right-hand side; in the case of the thermal decomposition of hydrogen iodide, on the other hand, there are two molecules on each side of the equation, and therefore no change in volume when the reaction takes place.

The effect of pressure on the position of equilibrium thus depends on the volume change, if any, which accompanies the reaction.

If a change in the equilibrium is brought about by external conditions the equilibrium is said to be mobile, and our conclusions on the effect of pressure can be formulated very generally by the so-called "principle of least constraint" which is linked with the names of le Chatelier and van't Hoff. It states that if a constraint is applied to a system in equilibrium, reaction will take place in such a way as to minimize the constraint. In the above-mentioned case of the oxides of nitrogen we apply a constraint in the form of pressure. The effect of the pressure is diminished if, under the influence of the pressure, the system decreases in volume. Therefore, in accordance with the principle of least constraint, pressure displaces the equilibrium in the direction of the system with the smaller volume. $2NO_2$ represents a volume twice as great as N_2O_4, so the equilibrium in the system

$$N_2O_4 \rightleftharpoons 2NO_2$$

is displaced from right to left by the application of pressure.

In the case

$$2HI \rightleftharpoons H_2 + I_2$$

there are equal volumes on both sides of the equation. Displacement of the equilibrium can thus have no effect on the applied constraint. The equilibrium is therefore unaffected by pressure.

(b) *Effect of temperature.* The principle of least constraint can also be applied to the effect of temperature on the equilibrium. If the reaction

$$A + B \rightarrow C$$

proceeds with the evolution of heat, the reaction is termed *exothermic* ; if, on the other hand, it proceeds with absorption of heat it is said to be *endothermic*. If, now, a constraint is applied to the reaction in the form of addition of heat that reaction will proceed which tends to minimize the constraint applied by minimizing the change of temperature. In other words, rise in temperature, i.e., addition of heat, will favour the endothermic reaction which absorbs heat, and vice versa. Thus the decomposition of an exothermic compound (one formed with evolution of heat) will be favoured by a rise in the temperature, while that of an endothermic compound will be favoured by a fall in the temperature. Of course, the extent of decomposition may be so slight at all temperatures (even although it changes as predicted) that this effect cannot be observed for a particular compound.

The principle of least constraint is quite general in its application. It applies equally to heterogeneous and to homogeneous reactions. Suppose we consider first a very simple example of heterogeneous equilibrium, viz., vapour and liquid. We know that for vaporization heat is necessary, so by applying heat to a liquid the equilibrium is displaced in the direction which takes in heat ; therefore with rising temperature vapour is formed, and the vapour pressure becomes greater.

An interesting example of a homogeneous reaction (from the technical point of view) is found in the reaction

$$N_2 + 3H_2 \rightleftharpoons 2NH_3.$$

Nitrogen and hydrogen combine at high temperatures (above 600°) fairly rapidly, but at high temperatures the equilibrium of this exothermic reaction is displaced very considerably towards the left, so that at the temperatures stated on p. 50 only small concentrations of ammonia are produced.

However, at 400° the reaction proceeds very slowly. The possibility of making ammonia from nitrogen and hydrogen is therefore limited by the following considerations : at high temperatures the elements hardly combine at all ; at low temperatures, where the equilibrium is

Temp.							% NH$_3$
914° C.	.	.	.	.	.	.	0·007
801° C.	.	.	.	.	.	.	0·011
772° C.	.	.	.	.	.	.	0·019
631° C.	.	.	.	.	.	.	0·036
561° C.	.	.	.	.	.	.	0·069
500° C.	.	.	.	.	.	.	0·128

more favourable to the formation of ammonia, the reaction proceeds too slowly. In the latter case, however, the reaction can be accelerated by a catalyst, and in the Haber process various metallic oxides are used for this purpose. The principle of le Chatelier and van't Hoff, however, shows us another way of achieving the desired result. It is clear from the equation for the reaction that the application of pressure will displace the equilibrium from left to right, because on the right-hand side of the equation we have the system with the smaller volume. At 400° and 100 atmospheres pressure the equilibrium mixture contains approximately 25 per cent. of ammonia. This ammonia can then be condensed at low temperatures, where, of course, the nitrogen gas is far from its condensing point. The Haber process is thus a typical example of the application of the principle of least constraint.

We have already stated that the equilibrium constant, K, is dependent on the temperature in a manner connected with the heat of reaction, Q, which is measured in calories per gram-molecule of reactant. The connection between K and Q is given by the following equation :

$$\frac{\mathrm{d} \log K}{\mathrm{d} T} = \frac{Q}{RT^2} \qquad \text{. . . . . (4)}$$

This equation can be deduced on the basis of thermodynamics. It is clear from the equation, and also, for that matter, directly from the principle of least constraint, that if the heat of reaction Q is zero, change of temperature will not affect the equilibrium constant. It should be mentioned that when heat is absorbed, Q is positive ; when it leaves the system, Q is negative.

Integration of the above expression gives the following result. At absolute temperatures T_1 and T_2 the corresponding equilibrium constants K_1 and K_2 are connected by the equation

$$\log \frac{K_1}{K_2} = \frac{Q}{R}\left(\frac{1}{T_2} - \frac{1}{T_1}\right).$$

In this expression it is supposed that Q is constant, i.e., that the heat of reaction is the same at different temperatures. Strictly speaking this is not the case, as is easily seen. To raise the temperatures of the original reactants and the reaction products quantities of heat will be required which will depend on the respective specific heats of these substances. Obviously the specific heats of different substances will be different, and hence the difference in heat content of the original substances and the reaction products will depend on temperature. Since this difference is precisely the heat of reaction, the latter will vary with temperature.

10. Thermochemistry. Hess's Law

The energy of activation can be calculated with the aid of Arrhenius' equation (see p. 36) if the reaction velocity at two different temperatures is known. The activation energy cannot be measured directly as it is connected with the energies of individual molecules, and does not depend solely on the average energy of all the molecules.

It is different with the heat of reaction. This is taken in from the surroundings (endothermic reaction) or given up to them (exothermic reaction), and can therefore be measured directly by carrying out the reaction in a calorimeter. There are, however, considerable practical difficulties if the reaction is either very slow or very rapid. On the other hand, if the reaction gives an equilibrium, and the equilibrium concentrations can easily be measured, it is possible to calculate the heat of reaction from the change of the equilibrium constant with temperature.

In many other cases Hess's law may be applied. This law is none other than the law of conservation of energy applied to chemical reactions, and states that if a reaction can be carried out in two different ways, the total heat of reaction is the same no matter which path is taken. An example will make this clear.

Hydrogen chloride can be made from hydrogen and chlorine by exposing a mixture of the gases to light. The reaction proceeds rapidly and is complete. The heat of reaction can be determined calorimetrically.

$$H_2 + Cl_2 \rightarrow 2HCl + 44,000 \text{ cal.}$$

Another method of making hydrogen chloride from its elements might be to combine first hydrogen and iodine together. The heat of this reaction can be obtained from the heat of sublimation of iodine and the heat of reaction between hydrogen and iodine vapour obtained from the law of van't Hoff applied to the equilibrium between H_2, I_2, and HI.

$$H_2 + I_2 \text{ (solid)} \rightarrow 2HI - 12,072 \text{ cal.}$$

The hydrogen iodide can then be made to react with chlorine in a calorimeter, when hydrogen chloride and solid iodine are formed.

$$2HI + Cl_2 \rightarrow I_2 \text{ (solid)} + 2HCl + 55,932 \text{ cal.}$$

The net result of the last two reactions is the production of 2HCl and the liberation of $55,932 - 12,072 = 43,860$ calories, in good agreement with the value obtained from the direct reaction.

Combustions usually take place rapidly and completely and the quantity of heat evolved can be readily measured. By using these values and applying Hess's law it is often possible to calculate the heat of a reaction which could not be determined directly.

As an example we may take the heat of formation of methane from its elements :

$$C + 2H_2 \rightarrow CH_4 + x \text{ cal.}$$

x can be found from the heats of combustion of carbon, hydrogen, and methane :

$$C + O_2 \rightarrow CO_2 + 96,960 \text{ cal.}$$
$$2H_2 + O_2 \rightarrow 2H_2O + 136,760 \text{ cal.}$$
$$CH_4 + 2O_2 \rightarrow CO_2 + 2H_2O + 214,700 \text{ cal.}$$

By adding the first two and subtracting the third we have

$$C + 2H_2 - CH_4 \rightarrow 19,020 \text{ cal.}$$
or $$C + 2H_2 \rightarrow CH_4 + 19,020 \text{ cal.}$$

The reaction is thus definitely exothermic.

By using Hess's law it is possible to find the calorific value of foods. The digestion of food in the body is a slow and complicated process, but the final products are carbon dioxide and water. The total amount of heat evolved is therefore the same as if the substance were completely burned.

Physiological experiments show that in the combustion of carbohydrates and fats in the body the amount of energy liberated is 4,100 and 9,400 calories per gm. respectively. When these substances are burned in a calorimeter the amounts of heat liberated are 4,200 and 9,500 calories per gm. respectively. The close agreement between the two values indicates the accuracy of the physiological experiment.

For proteins the physiological method gives 4·1 kcals per gm. as against 5·7 kcals per gm. by the physico-chemical method. The difference is completely explained by the fact that in the ordinary combustion of proteins the nitrogen is given off in the elementary state, whereas in digestion the nitrogen appears as urea.

CHAPTER III

ELECTROCHEMISTRY

1. Ions. Faraday's Law

It is commonly accepted that salts, acids and bases are dissociated into two or more parts when they are dissolved in water.

Support is given to this view by evidence from analytical chemistry. All sulphates give a precipitate of barium sulphate with barium chloride. All silver salts give a precipitate of silver iodide with potassium iodide. From these examples, to which could be added countless others, the conclusion is reached that the sulphates contain two constituents, a metal radical and a sulphate radical, and that all silver salts contain a silver radical and an acid radical.

Experiments on the conduction of an electric current by solutions of acids, bases, and salts have given rise to the view, which has been held for many years, that the current is conducted by means of ions ; these are actually the radicals of which the dissolved substance is composed, charged either positively or negatively. Their movement is concerned in the passage of the current.

If an electric current is passed through a metal wire the charge is transported through the metal of which the wire is composed without any chemical change taking place. If, however, an electric current is passed through a solution of a salt fundamental changes take place which show that the motion of the electricity is associated with a transport of matter. For example, if two platinum electrodes are placed in a solution of copper chloride and a current is passed through the solution, chlorine gas is liberated at the anode (positive electrode) and copper is deposited on the cathode (negative electrode). This phenomenon is best explained by assuming that the electric current is carried by positively charged copper ions and negatively charged chloride ions. The positive ions move towards the negative electrode (and are therefore called cations), whilst the negatively charged ions move towards the positive electrode (and are called anions).

Faraday discovered that if an electric current were passed through solutions of different salts the quantity of metal deposited was proportional to the quantity of electricity passed through the solution. In order to deposit one gram-equivalent of a substance 96,488 coulombs of electricity must be passed. Thus, 107·88 gm. of silver, 63·54/2 gm. of copper, etc., are deposited by 96,488 coulombs. The same result applies to the substance which is deposited or liberated at the anode.

The conclusion is thus reached that a molecule of a salt, when dissolved in water, is dissociated into a cation and an anion. These carry equal but opposite charges of electricity, the total charge carried by one gram-equivalent of a substance being always the same. In terms of the electron theory we can say that each negatively charged univalent ion carries with it one electron in excess, and each negatively charged bivalent ion two electrons in excess. A chloride ion thus carries one extra electron, a sulphate ion two. When an atom or radical becomes a univalent cation it loses one electron, and thus carries an excess positive charge numerically equal to the charge on the electron. Here again the number of positive charges in excess of the normal carried by a cation is equal to its valency. According to this view copper sulphate, for example, is dissociated into a cation which can be represented as Cu^{++} and an anion, which can be written SO_4^{--}.

2. Speed of the Ions

If an electric current is passed between two copper electrodes placed in a solution of copper sulphate we may picture what happens as follows : the positively charged copper ions move towards the cathode, the sulphate ions towards the anode. It follows that the solution in the neighbourhood of the anode would become poorer in copper ions if it were not for the fact that copper ions, equivalent to the sulphate ions remaining, enter the solution from the anode. On the other side, sulphate ions move across from the cathode to the anode, and the excess of copper ions remaining are deposited on the cathode. Thus, the net effect of the passage of the current is that copper is dissolved off the anode and is deposited on the cathode.

Do both ions move at the same speed ? One is inclined at first to answer this question in the affirmative, because it would seem that if the speed were not the same peculiar electrical potentials would arise in the solution. This idea is, however, quite incorrect, and this can be shown by reference to the sketch diagrams in Fig. 19. In the figures C and A are the two copper electrodes, cathode and anode, respectively. The space between the two is filled with water, containing copper and sulphate ions. This space we will divide into two parts, which we will call the cathode space and the anode space, respectively. The copper ions will be represented diagrammatically by • and the sulphate ions by o.

Let us consider the state of affairs represented in Fig. 19(a), where there are nine copper sulphate molecules in both the cathode and the anode compartments. (Of course, there might just as well be a million times as many, each dot then representing a million ions.)

Suppose now that the current has been passing sufficiently long for six copper ions to be deposited on the cathode. We will consider first the extreme case of velocity difference between the two ions, where the electricity is carried entirely by the copper ions, and the sulphate ions have zero velocity, i.e., they do not move at all.

The transport of the current then takes place as follows : each time a positively charged copper ion leaves the anode a copper ion is attracted towards and deposited on the cathode. Every time a copper ion is deposited an electric charge is given up to the cathode.

When this has happened six times we have the state of affairs represented in Fig. 19(b), where the dots next to the cathode show the number of copper atoms deposited, whilst the dots with arrows at the anode give the number of copper atoms that have gone into solution as

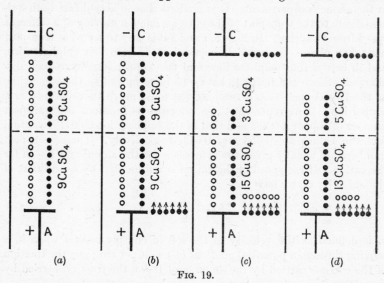

FIG. 19.

ions. It is clear from this diagram that the final stage is such that the concentration in the cathode and anode compartments remains unchanged.

Suppose we now consider the other extreme case, where the current is carried exclusively by the negatively charged ions * (see Fig. 19(c)). In this case each time a negatively charged sulphate ion leaves the cathode the sulphate ion arriving at the anode brings a copper atom into solution. It follows that at the cathode, from which six sulphate ions have left, six copper ions will be discharged and deposited. The final state is shown in Fig. 19(c), which agrees with Fig. 19(b) in so far as

* These ideas are not by any means so improbable as the reader may perhaps think, for such a transport of current by only one type of ion (so-called unipolar conduction) has been well substantiated, for example in many cases of conduction through crystals (solid electrolytes). In a silver chloride crystal for instance, the current is carried by the silver ions alone, and in a lead bromide crystal by the bromide ions alone.

E

six copper atoms go into solution at the anode, and six are deposited at the cathode, but the difference lies in the fact that only three copper and three sulphate ions now remain in the cathode department, while there are fifteen in the anode compartment. A considerable change in concentration has taken place.

Actually, however, neither Fig. *b* nor Fig. *c* gives the real state of affairs, which is intermediate between the states represented by these two diagrams. Fig. *d* gives a closer approximation to the truth. Here there is a difference of concentration in the two compartments, there being five molecules in the cathode compartment and thirteen in the anode compartment. It is obvious that in actual fact both ions contribute to the transport of the current, one ion moving at a different speed from the other. In Figs. *b*, *c* and *d* it is easy to see what transport has taken place. In case *b* six copper ions, in case *c* six sulphate ions, and in case *d* four sulphate ions and two copper ions have been discharged. Since the four sulphate ions have moved in the same time as the two copper ions, a sulphate ion must move twice as fast as a copper ion. If we represent these velocities as fractions the transport number of copper is 0·333 and that of the sulphate ion 0·667. In actual fact the values are 0·356 and 0·644, respectively. These transport numbers are usually given the symbols n for the anion, and $1 - n$ for the cation. If the speed of the cation is represented by v_c and that of the anion by v_a, we have

$$\frac{v_c}{v_a} = \frac{1 - n}{n}.$$

v_c is defined as the velocity of the ion in cm. per second when it is moving through a potential gradient of 1 volt per cm., n is the fraction of the current carried by the anion, and $1 - n$ the fraction carried by the cation.

These ideas are due to Hittorf, who in the years 1853–9 developed the fundamental theory which shows how the quotient of the ionic velocities can be obtained by the determination of the concentration changes in the cathode and anode compartments.

3. Electrical Conductivity

The transport of the electric current is thus effected by ions. Investigations of the resistance which the current experiences in passing through a solution, first carried out by Kohlrausch, have given a further insight into these phenomena. He measured the resistances of solutions by means of a Wheatstone's Bridge, represented diagrammatically below. AB is a metal wire 100 cm. long, C is a movable contact, W is a resistance box, and X is the cell in which the solution of which the resistivity is to be found is placed. T is a telephone and ac an accumulator which provides the primary current for a small induction coil. If, now, the sliding contact is moved until no current passes through the circuit CD (this is the case when the buzz of the induction coil reaches minimum intensity in the telephone), the wire AB will be divided into one piece of length L and another of length 100 — L. The ratio of the resistance in the box W to that of the cell X is then L : (100 — L).

Instead of the resistance in ohms, it is usual to give the conductivity (i.e., the reciprocal of the resistance) in reciprocal ohms (ohms^{-1}, or mhos). The specific conductivity, κ, of a solution is the conductivity of a centimetre cube of the solution, i.e., the conductivity of the solution when placed between two electrodes each of 1 sq. cm. area, and separated by a distance of 1 cm., or the conductivity of a cube of the

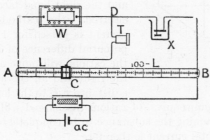

Fig. 20.

electrolyte of side 1 cm. If the concentration of the solution given as the number of gram-equivalents of the electrolyte contained in 1 c.c. of the solution is c, the equivalent conductivity, Λ, is defined as κ/c. This quantity is a measure, so to speak, of how much each gram-equivalent contributes to the conductivity. The molecular conductivity, μ, which has the same significance as the equivalent conductivity, Λ, except that it applies to one gram-molecule instead of one gram-equivalent, is also used.

Kohlrausch found the following results. The specific conductivity, κ, naturally depends on the concentration of the solution. The more molecules there are dissolved, the more ions there will be, and hence the more carriers of the electricity. The solution will, therefore, conduct better. If, however, the equivalent conductivity, Λ, is calculated it is found to become greater the more dilute is the solution, gradually approaching a limiting value, Λ_0, the so-called equivalent conductivity at infinite dilution. That is to say once the dilution is reached where $\Lambda = \Lambda_0$, further dilution has no effect on the equivalent conductivity.

Kohlrausch found that this quantity, Λ_0, could be calculated from the speed of the ions, the value of which is known from the experimental determinations of Hittorf. He showed that

$$\Lambda_0 = F(v_c + v_a)$$

where F is the Faraday and has the value 96,488 coulombs, as mentioned in § 1 of this chapter (p. 53), and v_c and v_a are the velocities of the cation and the anion respectively.

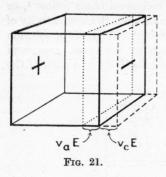

$v_a E$ $v_c E$

FIG. 21.

The proof of this relationship follows from a consideration of what happens to the ions in a cube of side 1 cm. filled with a solution of concentration c gm. equiv. per c.c. (Fig. 21). The left-hand face is the positive electrode (the anode) and the right-hand face is the negative electrode (the cathode). Suppose a current is passed for 1 second under a potential difference of E volts, then all the cations will move a distance $v_c E$ to the right and all the anions will move a distance $v_a E$ to the left. In this time the number of gm. equivs. of cations discharged will be $v_c E c$ and of anions $v_a E c$, assuming the substance to be completely dissociated into its ions. The total current is therefore

$$(v_c + v_a)\,EcF = i.$$

By Ohm's law

$$E = iR.$$

Since κ is the conductivity of a centimetre cube, the resistance of the cube we are considering will be $1/\kappa$. Hence

$$(v_c + v_a)\,F = \frac{1}{c}\cdot\frac{i}{E} = \frac{1}{c}\cdot\frac{1}{R} = \frac{\kappa}{c} = \Lambda$$

which is Kohlrausch's relationship given above.

From the quotient (p. 56) and the sum of the speed of the ions the values of v_c and v_a can be obtained. Thus, determinations with sodium chloride at 25° give

$$\frac{v_c}{v_a} = \frac{0\cdot396}{0\cdot604}$$

whilst $\Lambda_0 = 126\cdot45$ ohm^{-1} cm.^{2} gm.-equiv.$^{-1}$

Therefore $Fv_c = 50\cdot10$ and $Fv_a = 76\cdot35$. If $F = 96,488$ coulombs $v_c = 52\cdot0 \times 10^{-5}$ and $v_a = 79\cdot0 \times 10^{-5}$ cm. per sec. per volt per cm.

Often the quantity Fv is given in place of v itself. It is called the equivalent ionic conductivity, and the symbols λ_c and λ_a are used for it. Values for various ions at 25° and at very great dilution are given in the table below.

It is rather remarkable that the speeds of the different ions (with the exception of the hydrogen and hydroxyl ions) differ so little between themselves. This fact is even more striking if organic ions

Ion	λc	Ion	λa
Li^+	38·68	Cl^-	76·35
		B_r^-	78·14
Na^+	50·10	I^-	76·84
K^+	73·50	SCN^-	66·5
Rb^+	77·81	IO_3^-	38·9
Cs^+	77·26	ClO_3^-	64·6
$\frac{1}{2}Zn^{++}*$	52·8	NO_3^-	71·46
$\frac{1}{2}Cd^{++}$	54	$\frac{1}{2}SO_4^{--}$	80·0
$\frac{1}{2}Ca^{++}$	59·50	$\frac{1}{2}CO_3^{--}$	69·3
$\frac{1}{2}Ba^{++}$	63·63	OH^-	198·6
H^+	349·8	CH_3COO^-	40·9

are compared; here ions differing considerably in molecular weight have speeds which do not differ very much. Stokes' law (p. 6) does not hold, it is true, for single molecules, but a similar relation between the velocity (determined by the electric potential and the charge) and the size of the ion could, in fact, be expected. Yet strikingly enough, the order of speeds of the alkali metal ions (lithium to cæsium in the above table) is just the reverse of what would be expected *a priori*. The atomic volume is measured by the atomic weight multiplied by the specific volume (the reciprocal of the density). Now, of the alkali metals lithium has the smallest atomic volume and cæsium the largest. From Stokes' law lithium would be expected to have the largest and cæsium the smallest speed. A glance at the table above shows that the reverse is the case. Why then does the volume of the moving particles appear to differ from that which would be expected ? Various workers, notably Washburn, have put forward the view that the ions attract a certain number of water molecules to themselves, and form complexes with them. The water molecules thus travel with the ions in electrolytic transport. The presence of these water molecules naturally increases the size of the ion. This hydration more or less accounts for the absence of differences in speed which would otherwise exist between ions of different size.

* The symbol $\frac{1}{2}Zn^{++}$ means 1 gm. equivalent ($\frac{1}{2}$ gm.-ion) of zinc ions. The speed of a zinc ion under a potential gradient of 1 volt per cm. would thus be 52·8/96,488 cm. per sec.

From these considerations it is clear that the order in which the alkali metal ions take up water molecules is

$$Li^+ > Na^+ > K^+ > Rb^+ > Cs^+.$$

This is called the lyotropic series which is connected with the binding of water by the ions and which we shall meet again, both for anions and cations in Chapters VIII and XI.

More recent investigations have shown that the hydrogen ion in solution is always combined with one molecule of water. The ion is therefore sometimes written as H_3O^+ instead of H^+.

4. The Ionic Theory of Arrhenius and Ostwald

Arrhenius was the first to suggest that ions are not formed by the electric current, but exist in the solution whether or not any current is passed.

He was led to this view by the investigations of van't Hoff, to which reference has already been made in Chapter I. It was shown that for acids, bases, and salts—that is, for electrolytes—the laws of dilute solutions did not wholly apply. The osmotic pressure, elevation of the boiling point, and depression of the freezing point were, for electrolytes, too high. The number of gram-molecules had to be multiplied by a factor i, in order to obtain agreement between theory and experiment.

The fundamental concept of the ionic theory is as follows : in a solution of an electrolyte there are molecules, a number of which are dissociated into ions. If the electrolyte is represented by BA, where B is the cation and A the anion, the equilibrium

$$BA \rightleftharpoons B^+ + A^-$$

exists in the solution.

Applying the law of mass action to this equilibrium (p. 45), we have

$$\frac{C_{B^+} C_{A^-}}{C_{BA}} = K.$$

Let us suppose that of each gram molecule of BA a fraction α is dissociated into ions. Then each gram-molecule of BA will give rise to $[\alpha B^+ + \alpha A^- + (1 - \alpha)BA]N$ particles. It is thus clear that in place of the 1 gram-molecule with its N particles (p. 2) we shall have in the solution $(1 + \alpha)N$ particles. The i factor of van't Hoff must therefore be $(1 + \alpha)$.*

---

* If the electrolyte dissociates into more than two ions, say n ions,
$$i = n\alpha + (1 - \alpha), \text{ or } i = 1 + (n - 1)\alpha.$$

Substituting these values of the concentrations in the equation for the law of mass action we have

$$\text{for } C_{B^+} \frac{\alpha}{V}, \text{for } C_{A^-} \frac{\alpha}{V}, \text{ for } C_{BA} \frac{1-\alpha}{V}$$

if 1 gram-molecule is dissolved in V litres. We thus have

$$\frac{1}{V} \frac{\alpha^2}{1-\alpha} = K$$

an expression which is known as the *Ostwald dilution law*.* It is clear from this equation, in which K is constant for a given temperature, that the greater V becomes the nearer α approaches to 1. When V is infinite, α actually $= 1$.

In the light of this work we can now get a better idea of Kohlrausch's rule, which we met in the previous paragraph. Λ_0 is the equivalent conductivity when the molecules are completely dissociated into ions. It follows at once that the conductivity per gram-equivalent of dissolved electrolyte is in this case simply the quantity of electricity which is transported per second by the total number of cations and anions, that is $Fv_c + Fv_a$.

If we assume further that the conductivity of a solution is directly proportional to the number of free ions, we can find the ratio of the degree of dissociation, α, at two dilutions and thus obtain the ratio of the equivalent conductivities at the two dilutions. Thus

$$\frac{\alpha_{v1}}{\alpha_{v2}} = \frac{\Lambda_{v1}}{\Lambda_{v2}}$$

which, when one of the dilutions is infinite, becomes

$$\frac{\alpha_v}{\alpha_0} = \frac{\Lambda_v}{\Lambda_0} \text{ or, since } \alpha_0 = 1, \alpha_v = \frac{\Lambda_v}{\Lambda_0}.$$

Thus we have a method of obtaining the degree of dissociation, α, directly.

At first sight the theory of Arrhenius presents a number of difficulties. That a molecule of sodium chloride should break down in water into a sodium particle and a chlorine particle cannot be reconciled with our knowledge of the properties of metallic sodium and of gaseous chlorine. It must be remembered, however, that a sodium ion is a sodium atom with a positive electric charge and that a chloride ion is

* The above derivation as it stands holds for an electrolyte BA which gives rise only to two ions ($n = 2$; the electrolyte is said to be a binary electrolyte), such as NaCl. It is easy to see that the dilution law for n ions takes the form $\frac{1}{V^{n-1}} \cdot \frac{\alpha^n}{1-\alpha} = K$.

a chlorine atom with a negative electric charge. An atom consists of a positively charged nucleus surrounded by enough negatively charged electrons to balance the nuclear charge. Thus, the sodium atom has a nucleus with eleven positive charges, surrounded by eleven electrons arranged in three orbits or energy-levels, containing respectively two, eight and one electrons. When the single electron in the outermost orbit is lost, a sodium ion with unit net positive charge remains. Similarly, the chlorine atom has seventeen units of positive charge on the nucleus, and $2 + 8 + 7$ electrons around it. It can take up an extra electron in the outermost orbit to give the negatively charged chloride ion.

It is thus clear that the sodium atom and the sodium ion differ markedly in structure, and it is no wonder that the atom and the ion have very different chemical properties, the more so when it is remembered that it is the electrons in the outermost orbit which are of importance in deciding chemical properties.

The theory of Arrhenius gives, in general, a very satisfactory picture of electrolytes. Nevertheless, in the course of time, a number of observations have been made for which it does not supply an adequate explanation. It has been found that the Ostwald dilution law only holds for electrolytes which are but slightly dissociated into ions, such as most organic acids. The strong inorganic acids, and almost all salts, are very highly dissociated into ions, and the Ostwald dilution law does not apply to them.

In more recent years a new theory has been put forward to account for this and other facts. We shall deal with it later (p. 170).

5. Applications

The difference between strong and weak acids, according to the ionic theory, lies in the fact that when these acids are dissolved in water to give solutions of the same concentration the strong acid is highly dissociated and gives rise to many ions, while the weak acid is only slightly dissociated and gives comparatively few ions. The degree of dissociation, α, at a given dilution, or better, the constant, K, of the Ostwald dilution law for the acid concerned is thus a measure of the strength of the acid. This constant, K, is therefore called the dissociation constant (not to be confused with degree of dissociation). If, for example, zinc is allowed to act on solutions of acids of equivalent concentrations, it is found that the volume of hydrogen evolved in a given time is dependent on the strength of the acid as just defined.

There are a number of reactions which appear to be catalysed by hydrogen ions. One of these has already been mentioned, namely the inversion of cane sugar. It is found that the catalytic effect of an added acid is directly proportional to the hydrogen ion concentration.

Conversely, the concentration of hydrogen ions in a solution can be determined from the speed with which a cane sugar solution is inverted in the presence of the acid. Another reaction which is accelerated by the presence of hydrogen ions is the hydrolysis of diazoacetic ester :

$$\begin{array}{ccc} CH = \overset{+}{N} = \overset{-}{N} & & CH_2OH \\ | & + H_2O = & | & + N_2. \\ COOC_2H_5 & & COOC_2H_5 \end{array}$$

The rate of evolution of nitrogen is a measure of the hydrogen ion concentration.

Another application of the ionic theory is to be found in the explanation of heat of neutralization. For the neutralization of strong acids by strong bases, it is found that the heat of neutralization (per gm. equivalent of acid or base) is always about 13,000 calories, provided the solutions are sufficiently dilute. If the neutralization reaction is represented by the equations

$$NaOH + HCl = NaCl + H_2O$$
$$KOH + HNO_3 = KNO_3 + H_2O$$

there appears to be no reason why the formation of these products should give rise to the same evolution of heat in both cases. If, however, it is remembered that the dilute solutions actually contain no undissociated molecules, but only the ions arising from the molecules concerned, it is clear that the above equations may be written :

$$Na^+ + OH^- + H^+ + Cl^- \rightarrow Na^+ + Cl^- + H_2O$$
$$K^+ + OH^- + H^+ + NO_3^- \rightarrow K^+ + NO_3^- + H_2O.$$

In other words Na^+ and Cl^- (or K^+ and NO_3^-) actually play no part in the neutralization at all. They are present in just the same quantity before and after the reaction. Every neutralization (taking place between dilute solutions of strong acids and bases) can therefore be represented by the equation :

$$OH^- + H^+ \rightarrow H_2O + 13,360 \text{ cal.}$$

and since one reaction covers all neutralizations it is obvious that the same amount of heat will be evolved in each case.

It is not only for neutralization reactions that ionic equations of this type can be written ; they can be used for all reactions where the reactants are wholly, or almost completely, dissociated. We shall consider this point further in § 7.

6. Electrolytic Dissociation of Water. pH

In the equation written above for the neutralization of an acid by a base we have tacitly assumed that water itself is not dissociated into ions, although it might be expected to dissociate into hydroxyl and hydrogen ions according to the equation :

$$H_2O \rightleftharpoons H^+ + OH^-.$$

Experiments by Kohlrausch and others have shown that water is dissociated only to a very small degree. If we write the mass action equation for this reaction we have

$$\frac{[H^+][OH^-]}{[H_2O]} = K' \text{ or } [H^+][OH^-] = K_w,$$

since the concentration of the water, $[H_2O]$, is effectively constant. Experiment shows that the dissociation constant, K_w, has a value of about 10^{-14}. It is thus clear that in pure water the concentration of hydrogen ions and that of hydroxyl ions is 10^{-7} gm.-ion per litre.

In solutions of both acids and bases, that is, in solutions containing a preponderance of hydrogen or hydroxyl ions, respectively, the relationship

$$[H^+][OH^-] = K_w$$

must hold. We can therefore characterize such solutions by their hydrogen ion concentrations.

Hydrogen ion concentrations may vary between about unity (as in normal solutions of strong acids) and about 10^{-14} (as in normal solutions of strong bases). Thus, these quantities are often extremely small, and for convenience of working the so-called hydrogen ion exponent, or pH value (sometimes also written pH) is generally used instead of the actual hydrogen ion concentration*

Thus, for a hydrogen ion concentration of 10^{-7}, the pH is 7. In general, the pH is the power of 10 of the hydrogen ion concentration with the sign changed ; or it is the logarithm of the hydrogen ion concentration with a negative sign prefixed. Thus

$$pH = -\log_{10}[H^+].$$

Here are some examples :

What is the pH of a 0·01 N solution of hydrochloric acid ? Since hydrochloric acid is practically completely dissociated into ions 0·01 N hydrochloric acid must contain 0·01 gm.-equivalents of hydrogen ion per litre. In other words, the concentration of hydrogen ion, C_{H^+}, is 10^{-2}. The pH is thus 2.

What is the pH of 0·01 N caustic potash solution ? Caustic potash

---

* This method has other advantages over the use of the hydrogen ion concentration itself. For instance, a graph giving the relationship between some property and the hydrogen ion concentration of a solution, usually becomes more comprehensible when the variation is expressed in terms of pH rather than in terms of concentration, since physico-chemical properties often vary linearly with the logarithm of the hydrogen ion concentration.

is completely dissociated into ions. 0·01 N caustic potash will thus have a concentration of hydroxyl ions, C_{OH^-}, of 10^{-2}. Since

$$C_{H^+} \cdot C_{OH^-} = 10^{-14} \quad \ldots \ldots \ldots \quad (1)$$

the concentration of hydrogen ion in the solution must be 10^{-12}. The pH is therefore 12.

It is, of course, possible to define the pOH of a solution as the negative logarithm of the hydroxyl ion concentration. The two terms are connected by equation (1), and by taking logarithms of both sides we get

$$\log_{10} C_{H^+} + \log_{10} C_{OH^-} = -14$$
$$pH + pOH = 14.$$

It is clear then that a neutral solution has a pH of 7, an acid solution has a pH numerically less than 7, and an alkaline solution a pH numerically greater than 7.

Finally, here is a more complicated example. If the hydrogen ion concentration of a solution is 2×10^{-6}, what is the pH of the solution ? Answer : $pH = \quad [(\log_{10} 2) - 6] = -(0·3010 - 6) = 5·70$.

7. Hydrolysis

If a salt of a weak acid and a strong base is dissolved in water, the solution is alkaline. Potassium cyanide, for example, which is a salt of the weak acid hydrocyanic acid, reacts with water in the manner shown in the equation :

$$KCN + H_2O \rightleftharpoons KOH + HCN \quad \ldots \ldots \quad (2)$$

or, written as an ionic equation in the same way as we have done for the neutralization reaction on p. 63,

$$CN^- + H_2O \rightleftharpoons OH^- + HCN \quad \ldots \ldots \quad (3)$$

Where a salt is decomposed in this manner by water the phenomenon is called *hydrolysis* (from the Greek *hudor* = water).

We will now consider why a reaction of this kind takes place to a marked extent when the salt is one of a weak acid.

If we prepare a solution of sodium chloride in water we have present the sodium ions, Na^+, and the chlorine ions, Cl^-, from the salt, and hydrogen and hydroxyl ions from the water. Since, however, sodium chloride, sodium hydroxide, and hydrochloric acid are all of them strong electrolytes, such a solution contains, essentially, sodium and chloride ions only.

It is quite different, however, in the case of a solution of potassium cyanide in water. The salt is strongly dissociated, and so is potassium hydroxide, but hydrocyanic acid is a very weak acid, which means that its solution in water contains a high proportion of undissociated molecules. In this solution, then, the following equations must apply simultaneously :

$$\frac{[\text{H}^+][\text{CN}^-]}{[\text{HCN}]} = K_a \qquad [\text{H}^+][\text{OH}^-] = K_w$$

If the second equation is divided by the first we have

$$\frac{[\text{OH}^-][\text{HCN}]}{[\text{CN}^-]} = \frac{K_w}{K_a} = K_h \quad \ldots \ldots \quad (4)$$

where K_h is called the hydrolysis constant. Actually, as will be readily seen, this equation is simply that obtained by the application of the law of mass action to the reaction of equation (3).

It is clear from equation (3) that there are just as many hydroxyl ions formed as there are hydrocyanic acid molecules, so that

$$[\text{OH}^-] = [\text{HCN}].$$

Equation (4) can therefore be written as follows :

$$\frac{[\text{OH}^-]^2}{[\text{CN}^-]} = K_h \quad \ldots \ldots \quad (5)$$

Now K_w, as has been stated above, is, in round figures, 10^{-14}. K_a, the dissociation constant of hydrocyanic acid, is 10^{-10}, so the hydrolysis constant from equation (4) is

$$K_h = \frac{10^{-14}}{10^{-10}} = 10^{-4}.$$

In a normal solution of potassium cyanide the concentration of cyanide ions may be taken as 1.* From equation (5) it follows that $[\text{OH}^-]^2 = 10^{-4}$ or $[\text{OH}^-] = 0 \cdot 01$, and the pH is 12.

It will thus be understood that this solution reacts alkaline, and since there must be a quantity of hydrocyanic acid formed corresponding to that of hydroxyl ions present (see equation (3)), it is also clear that such a solution of potassium cyanide will smell strongly of hydrocyanic acid.

This indicates, then, that although the degree of dissociation of water may be small it exerts a profound influence on the properties of solutions of salts of weak acids. The same considerations as the above apply, of course, to the carbonates ; hence the alkaline reaction of a solution of washing soda.

An exactly similar argument can also be used in considering the salt of a strong acid and a weak base. Analogous reasoning leads to the fact that hydrolysis gives rise to an acidic solution. Thus, for example,

---

* Owing to the formation of undissociated HCN, some of the CN⁻ ions will be removed, but this amounts to not more than 1 per cent. of the total, and in an approximate calculation the effect on the result is negligible.

an aqueous solution of aluminium sulphate reacts acid owing to the weakness of the base, aluminium hydroxide, compared with the strength of sulphuric acid.

In the case of a salt formed from a weak acid and a weak base, it is obvious that it will undergo considerable hydrolysis when it is dissolved in water, but the solution will not exhibit either strong acidity or strong alkalinity.

The pH of body fluids is closely dependent on this phenomenon of hydrolysis. Actually the pH of these body fluids in the living organism always remains constant. The factors which bring about this constancy of pH will be examined in the following paragraph.

8. Buffer Mixtures

If it is desired to prepare a liquid which has a pH of, say, 2, that is a perfectly simple matter ; we have seen already on p. 64 that a 0·01 N solution of hydrochloric acid will have a pH of 2. Suppose, however, we wish to prepare a solution of pH 6, then such a solution could not be obtained merely by making a 10^{-6} N solution of hydrochloric acid. Traces of alkali dissolved from the glass are sufficient to alter markedly this small hydrogen ion concentration.

Similarly, it is simple enough to make a solution of pH 12 ; all that is necessary is to make a 0·01 N solution of sodium hydroxide. But, a very dilute solution of sodium hydroxide, which should have, say, a pH of 8, is markedly affected by the smallest traces of carbon dioxide in the air.

Yet it is of the greatest importance that we should be able to prepare solutions of a definite and constant hydrogen ion concentration. For this purpose buffer solutions are used. A buffer mixture can be prepared, for example, by mixing a solution of a weak acid with a salt of the same acid. Acetic acid and sodium acetate will serve. Suppose for the sake of convenience that we call the acid HA, and the salt MA, each letter in these symbols representing an ion, then, for a solution of the acid alone we have :

$$\frac{[H^+][A^-]}{[HA]} = K_a \text{ or } [H^+] = \frac{[HA]}{[A^-]} K_a.$$

If the salt MA is added to this solution, $[A^-]$ can be taken to be the concentration of the salt, C_{salt}, as the latter is completely dissociated, and its ionic concentration will greatly exceed that of the acid. Thus the addition of the salt will repress the dissociation of the acid very considerably. As $[A^-]$ becomes very great $[H^+]$ becomes much smaller. The salt containing $[A^-]$ thus depresses the dissociation of the acid considerably. Therefore [HA] can be replaced by the total concentration of the acid, C_{acid} ; $[H^+]$ is only a very small fraction of C_{acid}. We thus have

$$[H^+] = \frac{C_{acid}}{C_{salt}} \cdot K_a.$$

We can write this in another way by taking logarithms of both sides, and then reversing the signs, thus :

$$og_{10}[H^+] = \log_{10}\frac{C_{acid}}{C_{salt}} + \log_{10} K_a$$

or $$pH = pK_a + \log_{10}\frac{C_{salt}}{C_{acid}}$$

Here pK_a is defined similarly to pH as $-\log_{10} K_a$. We thus see that the pH is completely determined by the *ratio* of concentrations of the salt and the acid, but not by the concentration of the acid itself. In other words, a buffer mixture made from a salt and an acid in a definite ratio has a hydrogen ion concentration which is independent, within certain limits of dilution, of the quantity of water added. It is thus possible to prepare a buffer solution of a weak acid with one of its salts, and to calculate the pH of the solution from the concentrations and the dissociation constant of the acid.

It requires no further demonstration to show that it is possible to make buffer solutions with pH values greater than 7 from mixtures of a weak base and a suitable salt. The formula in this case is

$$pOH = pK_b + \log_{10}\frac{C_{salt}}{C_{base}}$$

or $$pH = 14 - pOH = 14 - \left[pK_b + \log_{10}\frac{C_{salt}}{C_{base}} \right]$$

In the table below, examples of such buffer solutions with their pH values are given.

Mixtures of CH_3COOH and CH_3COONa		Mixtures of NH_4OH and NH_4Cl	
Ratio acid/salt	pH	Ratio salt/base	pH
16 : 1	3·54	16 : 1	8·29
4 : 1	4·14	4 : 1	8·89
1 : 1	4·74	1 : 1	9·49
1 : 4	5·35	1 : 4	10·10
1 : 16	5·96	1 : 16	10·70
1 : 32	6·25	1 : 32	11·00

The above discussion gives us the explanation of an important property of buffer solutions. It has been shown that buffer solutions with a pH less than 7 are made from a weak acid, HA, and its salt, MA, and that the pH depends only on the ratio of the concentrations of the acid and the salt. What now will take place if to a buffer solution of, say, pH 5 (which therefore contains only 0·00001 of an equivalent of hydrogen ion per litre), a drop of concentrated hydrochloric acid (or a drop of a concentrated solution of sodium hydroxide) is added, with its large number of hydrogen (or hydroxyl) ions ? There will be little change in pH, since the added hydrogen or hydroxyl ions will react as follows with the components of the buffer solution :

$$H^+ + A^- \rightarrow HA$$
$$OH^- + HA \rightarrow H_2O + A^-.$$

The individual concentrations of acid and salt will therefore change, but their ratio—which is what determines the pH—will change only by a small amount. The solution is said to be " buffered." How much the ratio changes depends on how great the concentrations of acid and salt themselves are ; that is to say, on whether the small changes are larger or smaller fractions of C_{acid} or C_{salt}.

This all leads to the idea of buffer capacity. A solution containing 0·0001 N acid and 0·0001 N salt has a smaller buffering capacity than one containing 0·1 N acid and 0·1 N salt.*

The term buffer capacity can be given a quantitative significance by asking the question : How many equivalents of strong acid or strong base need to be added to 1 litre of a buffer solution to change the pH by one unit ? The buffer capacity is thus $\dfrac{dx}{dpH}$ where dx is the number of equivalents of strong acid or base which must be added to 1 litre of the buffer solution in order to change the pH by dpH.

The hydrogen ion concentration is a measure of what may be called the *true* acidity of the solution. It is well to distinguish this from the *potential* acidity, which is not determined by the hydrogen ion concentration, but by the total replaceable hydrogen present.

The difference will be appreciated from the following : suppose a solution of a weak acid, say acetic acid, of which only a small fraction of the acetic acid molecules are dissociated into ions, is titrated. Suppose that sodium hydroxide is added from a burette. Then the free hydrogen ions immediately react with the added hydroxyl ions, and immediately a further number of acetic acid molecules dissociate, so that the small hydrogen ion concentration remains unchanged.† This

---

* In addition, calculation shows that buffer capacity depends on the ratio $\dfrac{C_{acid}}{C_{salt}}$, the ratio 1 being the most favourable.

† We shall see on p. 80 that what actually happens in this case is rather more complicated than is stated here.

goes on until all the acetic acid is neutralized. Titration thus gives the potential acidity, while the real acidity, that is, the hydrogen ion concentration at the beginning of the titration, is not the determining factor. A solution of 0·1 N hydrochloric acid and one of 0·1 N acetic acid have the same potential degree of acidity, but the solution of the strong acid, hydrochloric acid, has many more hydrogen ions and has therefore a much higher real acidity and a numerically lower pH than the acetic acid.

For many biological problems it is the real acidity that is of greater significance than the potential acidity. It thus becomes a matter of some importance to investigate methods which are available for the determination of hydrogen ion concentration. These methods are widely used in physiological laboratories.

Before we can describe these methods however, (see p. 74, etc.), some other electrochemical questions must first be considered.

9. Electromotive Force and Electrode Potentials

Before dealing with the measurement of hydrogen ion concentrations, we must first see how the concentration of any ion in a solution can be determined.

One method we have already dealt with in the determination of electrical conductivity on p. 61. Here we obtained the connection between ionization and conductivity. If, however, we have a solution which contains a number of different electrolytes, it is impossible to determine all the contributing ionic concentrations from one determination of conductivity. We must, therefore, find a method which will enable us to determine the concentration of any particular ion in a mixture of a number of ionic species.

The voltaic cell and its electromotive force (e.m.f.) can help us to do this. A voltaic cell consists, in its simplest form, of a solution of an electrolyte in which are placed two electrodes of different metals. If the two electrodes are connected by a wire through a galvanometer it is observed that a current flows through the instrument. An electromotive force has been set up ; its nature will be discussed further.

This e.m.f. can be regarded as arising from the fact that each of the electrodes has a potential with respect to the electrolyte solution. The e.m.f. of the cell is the algebraic sum of the potential differences at each electrode.

We will first consider the cause of this potential difference between the electrode and the solution. Suppose we immerse a zinc rod in a solution of zinc sulphate, containing zinc ions. Zinc ions will pass both from the metal to the solution and from the solution to the metal, and equilibrium will be reached when the rates of these two processes are equal :

$$Zn \text{ (metal)} \rightleftharpoons Zn^{++} \text{ (solution)} + 2e \text{ (metal)}.$$

There will now be a certain potential difference between the zinc rod and the solution, determined by the excess of electrons left on the rod, and called the electrode potential. The equilibrium position—and hence the " concentration " of electrons on the metal, and the electrode potential—will obviously depend on the inherent tendency of the metal to give ions in solution, and on the concentration of the ions already in solution. When this concentration is unity (1 gm.-ion per litre), the electrode potential is called the " standard electrode potential," and this is a definite quantity, characteristic of zinc or of any other metal.

A single electrode potential of this type, though of considerable theoretical importance, has no practical meaning as it cannot be measured. The best we can do is to combine the electrode under consideration with some other electrode to make a cell, of which the electromotive force can be determined. This will be the algebraic sum of the electrode potentials of the two electrodes used to make up the cell.

One of the electrodes can be a standard electrode of some kind, such as the calomel electrode (p. 75), to which some arbitrary potential may be ascribed. We can, if we like, call this arbitrary potential zero. By making up cells with various electrodes and a standard electrode, we can obtain the relative values of the electrode potentials, but not their actual values.

We have mentioned that the electrode potential depends upon the concentration of the ions in the solution in which the electrode is immersed. We can therefore construct a cell of which the electrodes are of the same metal, but are placed in solutions of ions of the metal of different concentrations. Such an arrangement is called a concentration cell.

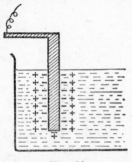

FIG. 22.

Suppose we have two electrodes of a metal M placed in solutions of ions of M of concentration c_1 and c_2, separated by a porous partition. Suppose the valency of the ions is n. We can deduce a formula for the e.m.f. of such a cell by remembering that if there are two ways of carrying out a change, the work done in the two methods must be the same. Otherwise it would be possible to go from one set of conditions by one route and back again by another and have a surplus of energy in hand. This would be contrary to one of the fundamental laws of nature—the law of conservation of energy.

Suppose that 1 gm.-atom of metal is dissolved off one electrode of a concentration cell, and deposited on the other. To do this electrically nF coulombs of electricity would be required, where F is the Faraday

(96,488 coulombs). The electrical work done would be $nF(E_1 - E_2)$, where E_1 and E_2 are the electrode potentials of the two electrodes, and $(E_1 - E_2)$ is thus the e.m.f. of the cell.

The same process of transferring a gm.-ion of metal ions from one concentration to another can be done osmotically, when work will be done against the osmotic pressure. Let us suppose that the osmotic pressure π of the ions is given by the equation $\pi = RTc$, where c is the concentration of the solution in gm.-ions per unit volume. Then the work done is $\int_{v_1}^{v_2} \pi dv$, where v_1 and v_2 are the volumes containing 1 gm.-ion, and are therefore the reciprocals of c_1 and c_2.

$$\int_{v_1}^{v_2} \pi dv = \int_{v_1}^{v_2} \frac{RT}{v} \, dv = RT \log \frac{v_2}{v_1} = RT \log \frac{c_1}{c_2}.$$

These two amounts of work—the electrical work and the osmotic work—must be equal. Hence

$$nF(E_1 - E_2) = RT \log \frac{c_1}{c_2},$$

$$\text{or } E_1 - E_2 = \frac{RT}{nF} \log \frac{c_1}{c_2}. \quad . \quad . \quad . \quad . \quad . \quad (6)$$

If we now let $c_2 = 1$, then E_2, by the above definition, is the standard electrode potential of the metal, which is given the symbol E^0. Substituting in the last equation (and putting $c_1 = c$, $E_1 = E$) we obtain the very important equation first derived by Nernst :

$$E = E^0 + \frac{RT}{nF} \log c$$

$$= E^0 + 2 \cdot 303 \, \frac{RT}{nF} \log_{10} c \quad . \quad . \quad . \quad . \quad (7)$$

This gives the dependence of the electrode potential of a metal on the concentration of its ions, in the solution with which it is in contact. Increasing this concentration will make the potential more positive. This is consistent with the above explanation since if we increase the concentration of zinc ions (in the example discussed) we shall displace the equilibrium position to the left, thus reducing the excess of electrons on the zinc rod and hence increasing the (positive) potential of the rod with respect to the solution.

The value of the constant factor $2 \cdot 303 \, RT/F$ is often required in calculations. At 18° C., 20° C. and 25° C. it has respectively the values $0 \cdot 0577$, $0 \cdot 0581$ and $0 \cdot 0591$. For many purposes, however, it is good enough to take it as $0 \cdot 058$ at room temperature.

There is something else, however, to be taken into account. The two solutions of concentration c_1 and c_2 are in contact. Since the cation and the anion move with different speeds, there will be a third potential, called a diffusion potential, at the surface of contact of the two solutions. This is caused by the unequal velocities of the ions across the surface of contact, which produce an unequal distribution of charge. Nernst has shown that the magnitude of this diffusion potential, $E_{\text{diff.}}$, is given by

$$E_{\text{diff.}} = \frac{RT}{nF} \frac{v_c - v_a}{v_c + v_a} \log \frac{c_2}{c_1}.$$

It has been found that this potential can be virtually eliminated by the use of intermediate " bridge " solutions such as saturated solutions of potassium chloride or ammonium nitrate, in which the speeds of the cation and the anion are nearly equal ($v_c - v_a \leftharpoonup 0$).

As stated above, it is not possible to determine the potential of a single electrode ; it is necessary to measure the difference of potential between two electrodes. The potential of any given electrode can be measured by comparing it with that of a so-called reference electrode, that is, a combination of an electrode and a solution with a known, constant potential difference between them.

We see from equation (7) that it is necessary for the metal concerned to be placed in a solution of constant ionic concentration, c. This constancy can best be obtained by using a saturated solution in contact with crystals of the solute. Copper in a saturated solution of copper sulphate in which crystals of $CuSO_4,5H_2O$ are present, for instance, will serve the purpose. In practice, however, it is better to use mercury in a paste of calomel (mercurous chloride, Hg_2Cl_2), or of mercurous sulphate (Hg_2SO_4).

A standard cell, used as a standard for e.m.f., is an element which is constructed from two such invariable electrodes, such as the

Weston cell :   Cd amalgam | satd. $CdSO_4$ soln. | Hg_2SO_4 | Hg.
Clark cell :   Zn amalgam | satd. $ZnSO_4$ soln. | Hg_2SO_4 | Hg.

The calomel electrode—mercury in contact with a saturated solution of mercurous chloride—can thus be used as a reference electrode, but calomel is so slightly soluble that its saturated solution has only a very small conductivity. Potassium chloride is therefore added, and this also has the effect of depressing the mercurous ion concentration, (see p. 86), thus changing the potential of the electrode. It is therefore necessary to specify the concentration of the potassium chloride, and one then has decinormal, normal and saturated calomel electrodes, depending on whether the potassium chloride solution is decinormal, normal or saturated. In practice, the electrode consists of a paste of metallic mercury and mercurous chloride, in contact with the appropriate potassium chloride solution.

10. The Hydrogen Electrode, the Hydrogen Scale, and the Determination of pH

A very important reference electrode is the hydrogen electrode. This consists of a platinum electrode on which finely-divided platinum has been deposited electrolytically (platinum black). Hydrogen is bubbled into the solution around the electrode, and the platinum black catalyses the attainment of the equilibrium :

$$\tfrac{1}{2}H_2 \text{ (gas)} \rightleftharpoons H^+ \text{ (soln.)} + e \text{ (on platinum).}$$

The position of this equilibrium, and hence the potential of the electrode, depends both on the pressure of the hydrogen gas and on the hydrogen ion concentration of the solution. The standard hydrogen electrode is that for which the hydrogen is at a pressure of one atmosphere and the solution is of unit hydrogen ion concentration. The potential of the standard hydrogen electrode is arbitrarily taken as zero and serves to define the hydrogen scale of electrode potentials.

If we combine a metal electrode, say a zinc electrode (consisting of a zinc plate immersed in a molar solution of zinc ions), with a standard hydrogen electrode and measure the e.m.f. of the cell thus produced, we obtain the difference between the standard electrode potentials of the metal and hydrogen. Since the latter has been taken arbitrarily as zero, the e.m.f. of the cell may be said to be the electrode potential of zinc on the hydrogen scale.

In this way we can find the standard electrode potentials of the various metals. The following are representative values :

	Volts.
Zn/Zn^{++}	-0.76
Fe/Fe^{++}	-0.44
Cd/Cd^{++}	-0.40
Sn/Sn^{++}	-0.14
Pb/Pb^{++}	-0.12
H_2/H^+	0.00
Cu/Cu^{++}	$+0.34$
Hg/Hg_2^{++}	$+0.80$
Ag/Ag^+	$+0.80$
Au/Au^{+++}	$+1.36$

This arrangement of the metals is known as the *electrochemical series*, or the *potential series* of the metals. The base metals are at the top of the table, and the noble metals at the bottom. It should be noted that the sign of the potential has no absolute significance ; if a

metal has a negative potential this means that its potential when in
contact with a molar solution of its ions is more negative than that
of the standard hydrogen electrode—and *vice versa*. The higher a
metal comes in the table—i.e., the more negative is its standard electrode potential—the greater will be the excess of electrons on it under
the standard conditions. But the actual charge is not known; a metal
may very well have a positive electrode potential as defined above, and
still be negatively charged with respect to the solution.

If the standard hydrogen electrode is placed in connection with
another hydrogen electrode in a solution of hydrogen ions of concentration c_H, we have a typical concentration cell, of which the e.m.f. is
given by the usual formula. If the potential of the standard hydrogen
electrode is E_o and that of the other electrode is E_c, the e.m.f. of the
cell $(E_c - E_o)$ is given by

$$E_c - E_o = \frac{RT}{nF} \log \frac{c_H}{1} = 2 \cdot 303 \frac{RT}{nF} \log_{10} c_H,$$

(since the concentration of hydrogen ions in the standard electrode is 1).

At 18° the factor $2 \cdot 303 \frac{RT}{nF}$ in this equation has the value $0 \cdot 0577$,

remembering that for hydrogen $n = 1$.

Thus $\quad\quad\quad -\log_{10} c_H = \dfrac{E_o - E_c}{0 \cdot 0577} = \mathrm{pH}$ . . . . (8)

We thus see that if $E_o - E_c = 57 \cdot 7$ millivolts (i.e. $0 \cdot 0577$ volt) the
pH $= 1$; if $E_o - E_c = 2 \times 57 \cdot 7$ millivolts, then the pH is 2, and so
on. In general, each $57 \cdot 7$ millivolt difference of potential represents
one unit of pH.

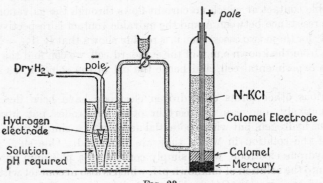

Fig. 23.

When an actual standard hydrogen electrode is used, E_0 is, of course, zero. But it is equally possible to combine the hydrogen electrode in the solution of unknown pH with some other reference electrode such as the calomel electrode. The potential of this electrode on the hydrogen scale can be found—if it is not already known—by making a preliminary calibration with a solution of known pH. Similarly, electrode potentials of metals are often determined with reference to the convenient calomel electrode, and the values subsequently converted to the hydrogen scale. At 25° C., the potentials of the decinormal, normal and saturated calomel electrodes are respectively $+ 0.33$ volts, $+ 0.28$ volts, and $+ 0.24$ volts on the hydrogen scale.

It is thus clear that the hydrogen electrode enables us to determine the pH of a solution directly. Fig. 23 is a diagram of a hydrogen electrode which consists of a platinum electrode immersed in the liquid of which the pH is to be determined in such a way that hydrogen can be passed into the solution around the electrode. The hydrogen electrode is combined with a normal calomel electrode (p. 73). The

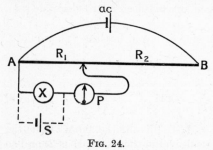

FIG. 24.

e.m.f. of the combination is measured by means of a potentiometer, of which a diagram is given in Fig. 24. R_1 and R_2 are two resistances, either two resistance boxes or two parts of a straight resistance wire, and the arrow represents a movable contact.

Either the experimental cell X or a standard cell S can be placed in series with the galvanometer P, as shown. An accumulator ac provides the current. A balance point is found, first for the standard cell and then for the experimental cell ; this is a position of the movable contact at which no current flows through the galvanometer. If the resistance between A and the movable contact is respectively R_s and R_x for these two cases, then it is readily shown that $R_s/R_x = E_s/E_x$. Thus, from the known e.m.f. of the standard cell, we can find the e.m.f. of the experimental cell, and hence the pH of the solution, as shown above.

Various other forms of hydrogen electrode have been described. Alternatively, one can use certain other electrodes not involving gaseous hydrogen, but whose potential depends in a simple way on the pH of the solution in which they are immersed. One such is the quinhydrone electrode, which simply consists of a platinum wire dipping into the solution of unknown pH, which is also in contact with solid quinhydrone crystals. Quinhydrone is a solid compound of one molecule of quinone with one of hydroquinone, and there is an oxidation-reduction equilibrium (see § 13) between these compounds :

Quinone   Hydroquinone

It is evident that the pH of the solution must affect the above equilibria, and it can be shown that the potential of the quinhydrone electrode varies linearly with pH, in the same way as does that of the hydrogen electrode itself. The electrode is calibrated with a solution of known pH, and gives reliable results as long as the pH is not greater than about 8.

In some cases it is impossible to carry out determinations with the hydrogen electrode because the substance present poisons the electrode. If, for example, hydrogen sulphide is present in the liquid to be tested, it reacts with the platinum and gives rise to platinum sulphide, thus making the determination impossible. Also, oxidizing agents which may be present have a disturbing effect because they oxidize the hydrogen, a reaction which is catalysed by the platinum.

There is, however, another method which can be used. It has been found that ordinary glass can behave as a hydrogen electrode. A very thin bulb is blown on a glass tube so that its electrical resistance is not too high, and in the bulb is placed an electrolyte which conducts well and in which an electrode is immersed. The potential of the electrode is then found to depend in the same way as that of the simple hydrogen electrode, on the pH of the solution in which the glass bulb is immersed. A calomel electrode is generally used as the reference electrode, and it is necessary to measure the e.m.f. of the combination by means of a suitable electronic circuit, because of the very high resistance introduced by the glass bulb. Once again calibration is effected with solutions of known pH.

11. Indicator Methods for the Determination of pH

The pH can also be determined in an entirely different way, namely by means of indicators.

An acid-base indicator is a weak organic acid, generally of a rather complex structure ; the colour of the undissociated acid molecules is different from the colour of the ions. There is an equilibrium between the acid and its ions :

$$HA \rightleftharpoons H^+ + A^-,$$

whose position will depend on the hydrogen ion concentration of the solution. Thus, in strongly acid solutions the dissociation of the indicator will be completely repressed, and the colour will be that of HA. In strongly alkaline solutions, on the other hand, the dissociation will be complete and the colour will be that of A⁻. By applying the law of mass action

$$K = \frac{[A^-][H^+]}{[HA]}$$

to the above equilibrium it is easily shown that appreciable amounts of HA and A⁻ will be in equilibrium with each other over a pH range of about 2 units. The colour of the indicator is determined by the ratio of A⁻ and HA and at about a 10-fold excess of the one over the other the colour change will be virtually complete. To go from a ratio $\frac{A^-}{HA} = 10$ to $\frac{A^-}{HA} = \frac{1}{10}$ the H⁺ concentration has to change by a factor

of 100 or the pH must decrease by 2 units. It is over this range that the colour will change, gradually, from that characteristic of HA to that characteristic of A⁻. Thus the indicator may change colour on either the acid or the alkaline side of neutrality (pH 7), and for only a few indicators (e.g., neutral red or bromothymol blue) will the colour change occur around the neutral point.

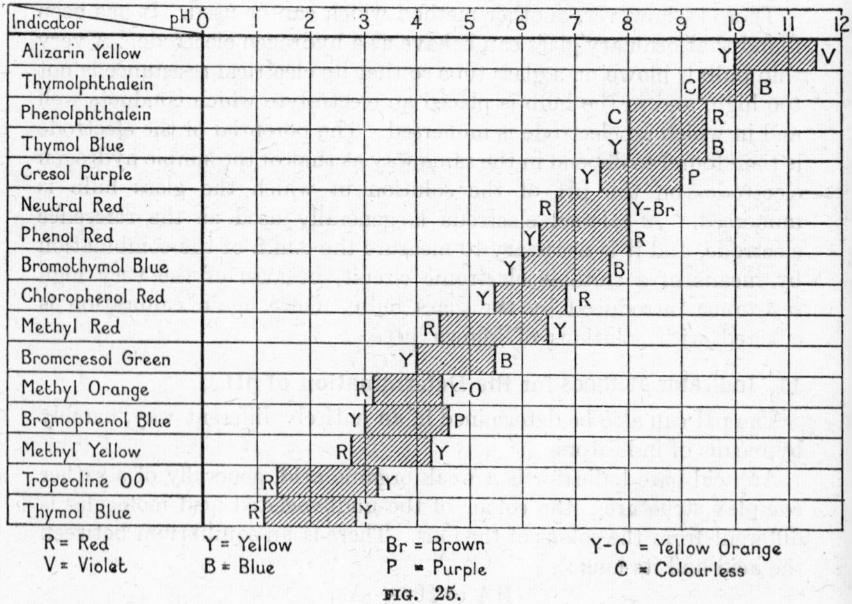

Indicator pH	0	1	2	3	4	5	6	7	8	9	10	11	12
Alizarin Yellow											Y		V
Thymolphthalein										C	B		
Phenolphthalein									C		R		
Thymol Blue									Y		B		
Cresol Purple								Y		P			
Neutral Red							R		Y-Br				
Phenol Red							Y		R				
Bromothymol Blue							Y	B					
Chlorophenol Red						Y		R					
Methyl Red					R		Y						
Bromcresol Green					Y	B							
Methyl Orange				R	Y-O								
Bromophenol Blue				Y	P								
Methyl Yellow				R	Y								
Tropeoline OO		R	Y										
Thymol Blue		R	Y										

R = Red   Y = Yellow   Br = Brown   Y-O = Yellow Orange
V = Violet   B = Blue   P = Purple   C = Colourless

FIG. 25.

Fig. 25 shows diagrammatically the pH ranges over which certain indicators change colour. In the case of methyl orange, for example, its colour at pH 3·1 is red, and at pH 4·3 orange-yellow. For pH values between these limits there are intermediate tints. Fig. 25 also indicates what a large selection of indicators is available, and how the colour changes of these indicators cover the whole field from pH 1 to pH 12.

Suppose now, for example, it is desired to find the pH of a solution which does not turn methyl orange completely red, nor completely orange. Buffer solutions (p. 67 are prepared which have pH values between 3 and 4·3. A few drops of methyl orange are added, and so a series of tubes is prepared with all shades of colour from red to orange. Methyl orange is also added to the solution of which the pH is required, and the standard tube which it matches is found. Obviously a fixed amount of indicator must be added to a fixed volume of each solution. This gives the pH.

One of the difficulties in applying the indicator method arises from the fact that the hydrogen ion concentration for which an indicator changes colour is often strongly modified by the presence of neutral salts or (as in biological fluids) of substances such as proteins. This error is referred to as the salt error or the protein error. Thus, the indicator method cannot entirely replace the hydrogen electrode method.

Within recent years much interest has been taken by biologists in the measurement of pH, as it has been discovered that various phenomena occurring with living organisms are connected with a very definite hydrogen ion concentration. Thus, an enzyme is effective only between certain pH limits, which are specific for each enzyme. The ability of the soil to promote satisfactory growth of certain crops depends on its pH, etc.

12. Titration of Acids and Bases and the Indicators Used

The work covered in the preceding paragraphs is necessary for the clear understanding of what takes place in the titration of acids and bases. The titration value is, of course, determined by what we have called the potential acidity, but in this paragraph we shall be concerned with showing how the pH changes during the titration.

Fig. 25 shows that the colour change of relatively few indicators occurs around the neutral point of pH 7. An indicator such as phenolphthalein changes colour at about pH 9. If therefore an alkaline solution is neutralized by the addition of acid in the presence of this indicator, the colour change occurs at pH 9, and before the liquid is actually neutral.

We shall now show how the pH of the solution changes in the course of a neutralization reaction. Let us consider first the case of a strong acid which is being neutralized by a strong base.

Suppose we determine the pH for mixtures of hydrochloric acid and sodium hydroxide, the initial concentration of each solution being 0·1 N.

The result is shown graphically in Fig. 26. The ordinates represent pH values and the volume of alkali added is given along the horizontal axis. Our original solution, 10 ml. of 0·1 N hydrochloric acid, has of course a pH of about 1. Addition of alkali, i.e., formation of sodium chloride, will have little effect on the pH, since the hydrogen ion concentration changes in direct proportion to the amount of free hydrochloric acid. As, however, we approach the neutral stage, the change in the hydrogen ion concentration, and therefore of the pH, becomes considerable. Since sodium chloride is not hydrolysed, the value of the pH will become 7 when exactly 10 ml. of alkali has been added.

If, conversely, one had started with the base and had added the hydrochloric acid to it, the curve would have taken the same course as shown in the lower half of Fig. 26.

If in place of the strong acid, hydrochloric acid, we had used the weak acid, acetic acid, as the starting substance, the shape of the curve would have been very different (Fig. 26). The first point is that 0·1 N acetic acid is less dissociated than 0·1 N hydrochloric acid, and thus has initially a higher pH value. If sodium hydroxide is now added sodium acetate is formed which is markedly hydrolysed (p. 65). The hydrogen ion concentration of the liquid thus does not change proportionately with the concentration of the acid, but in a manner which we have discussed more fully on p. 67. The shape of the curve can be fully understood by reference to buffer action. Sodium acetate in 0·1 N solution has a pH of 8·9 in consequence of hydrolysis. The mixing of equimolecular quantities of acid and caustic soda, therefore, results in a solution with a pH, not of 7, but of 8·9. The solution therefore has a pH of 7 before the end-point of the titration has been reached.

No further explanation should be required for the curve which represents the neutralization of hydrochloric acid with the weak base ammonia.

In the diagrams the values of the pH where the characteristic colour

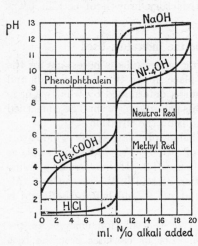

FIG. 26.

changes of three indicators take place, are given, viz., methyl red (pH 5), neutral red (pH 7) and phenolphthalein (pH 9). A consideration of the curves will show how these three indicators will respond for different ratios of acid and alkali in relation to the strength of the acid and base used.

If a strong acid is titrated with a strong base there is no difficulty since from Fig. 26 the whole distance between pH 4 and pH 10 is covered by a very small difference in composition. It is quite different, however, if hydrochloric acid is titrated with ammonia. Ammonium chloride, the salt of a strong acid and a weak base, has an acid reaction due to hydrolysis. Hence we must use an indicator such as methyl orange, which changes colour on the acid side of neutrality, and in the region where the titration curve is steep. Phenolphthalein would be quite useless, since it would change colour (at about pH 9) only after excess of ammonium hydroxide had been added. Moreover, the pH changes only slowly in the region of pH 9, so that the colour change would not be sharp.

For polybasic acids, such as phosphoric acid, there are different ionization stages to take into account. Phosphoric acid, H_3PO_4, can successively dissociate into the following ions :

$$H^+ + H_2PO_4{}^-, \quad 2H^+ + HPO_4{}^{--} \text{ and } 3H^+ + PO_4{}^{---}.$$

The dissociation constant for each of these equilibria is different, so that, with respect to the first ionization, the acid is a strong acid, with respect to the second it is weaker, and with respect to the third, weaker still. Fig. 27 represents the neutralization of phosphoric acid by caustic soda. If this curve is compared with the previous Fig. 26 an

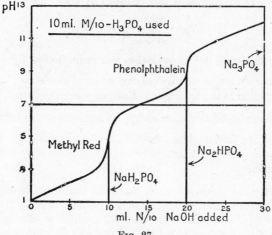

Fig. 27.

idea is obtained of the peculiar properties of these phosphate-phosphoric acid mixtures, and their characteristic buffer action, which enters frequently into phenomena connected with living organisms. The further discussion of these curves is left to the reader.

It remains to be noted that it is possible to carry out titrations very satisfactorily without the use of indicators, but with the aid of the hydrogen electrode, which is placed in the liquid to be titrated. The potential (with respect to the comparison electrode which must also be connected with the liquid being titrated) is noted after each addition, and a curve is obtained like those given in Figs. 26 or 27. It is seen from equation (8), p. 75, that $E_c - E_o$ is directly proportional to the pH. From the curve obtained the volume of acid or alkali added at neutralization is determined. This method is called potentiometric titration.

13. Reduction and Oxidation Potentials (Redox Potentials)

By the electrical method not only can we determine real acidities, and the strength of an acid or a base, but we can also find the oxidizing or reducing power of a solution. In order to understand the connection that exists between oxidation and reduction and electricity, we will consider the difference between a ferrous and a ferric salt.

We learn in elementary inorganic chemistry that iron forms an oxide FeO, which on oxidation is converted into Fe_2O_3. By dissolving these oxides in an acid we obtain a ferrous (Fe^{++}) salt and a ferric (Fe^{+++}) salt, respectively. It is said that Fe^{++} can be oxidized to Fe^{+++}, and conversely Fe^{+++} can be reduced to Fe^{++} although no oxygen is added or given up. These ions differ only in charge. The ferric ion has one positive charge more, and therefore one electron less than the ferrous ion. If we represent this electron by e we can write

$$Fe^{++} \underset{\text{reduction}}{\overset{\text{oxidation}}{\rightleftharpoons}} Fe^{+++} + e.$$

We may therefore define oxidation and reduction as follows :

oxidation is the removal of one or more electrons ;
reduction is the taking up of one or more electrons.

Other examples of oxidation-reduction systems are as follows :

Ferrocyanide-ferricyanide : $Fe(CN)_6^{----} \rightleftharpoons Fe(CN)_6^{---} + e$
Manganous-permanganate: $Mn^{++} + 4H_2O \rightleftharpoons MnO_4^- + 8H^+ + 5e$
Iodide-iodine : $\qquad I^- \rightleftharpoons \frac{1}{2}I_2 + e$

We know that there are weak and that there are strong oxidizing agents. How may this fact be expressed quantitatively ?

By " affinity " we mean the ease with which a reaction can take place, and it can be shown that the affinity of a reaction is measured by the useful work it can be made to perform. If the reaction can take place in an electric cell, then the affinity is given by the maximum electrical work which the cell can do. Thus, the affinity of the reaction

$$Zn + CuSO_4 \rightarrow Cu + ZnSO_4$$
(more accurately written : $Zn + Cu^{++} \rightarrow Zn^{++} + Cu$)

is to be measured by the e.m.f. of a Daniell cell, in which it is the cell reaction.

Zn electrode | ZnSO$_4$ solution | CuSO$_4$ solution | Cu electrode.

The electrical work is the potential difference multiplied by the quantity of electricity carried. We know from Faraday's law that the quantity of electricity required to change 1 gram-equivalent of a metal into the corresponding ion is 96,488 coulombs (p. 53). The potential difference, or the e.m.f. of the cell in which the reaction takes place, is thus a measure of the affinity of the reaction.

Consider now a platinum electrode immersed in a solution of ferrous and ferric ions. Platinum has such a high positive electrode potential that it may be considered an inert conductor—merely a source and reservoir of electrons. The platinum will acquire a definite potential with respect to the solution, because of the equilibrium :

$$Fe^{++} \rightleftharpoons Fe^{+++} + e \text{ (on platinum)}.$$

If we now increase the concentration of ferrous ions, we shall displace the equilibrium to the right, and the potential of the platinum will become more negative, since more electrons will have been released. Conversely, an increase in the ferric iron concentration will make the potential more positive. This effect of concentration on the potential is summed up in the following equation, which is readily deduced by the methods of thermodynamics :

$$E = E^0 + \frac{RT}{nF} \log \frac{[Ox]}{[Red]} \quad \cdot \quad \cdot \quad \cdot \quad \cdot \quad \cdot \quad (9)$$

Here E is the potential of the electrode with respect to the solution, [Ox] and [Red] are the concentrations of the oxidized and reduced forms (in the present example ferric and ferrous ions respectively), and n the number of electrons concerned in the equilibrium ($n = 1$ for the ferrous-ferric system). E^0 is the standard oxidation-reduction (or " redox ") potential for the system and, as can be seen, it is the potential established when the concentrations of oxidized and reduced forms are equal. These potentials are determined experimentally by combining the oxidation-reduction electrode with a hydrogen or calomel electrode, and the values of E^0 are then expressed on the hydrogen scale, in the usual way.　The table below gives some values of normal redox-potentials (E^0) at 25°.　Some of these are of biological importance.

$\frac{1}{2}H_2/H^+$ (at pH = 7)	-0.42 volt
Cr^{++}/Cr^{+++}	-0.41 ,,
V^{++}/V^{+++}	-0.26 ,,
Lactic acid/pyruvic acid $+ 2H^+$ (at pH = 7) .	-0.18 ,,
Succinic acid/fumaric acid $+ 2H^+$ (at pH = 7)	0.0 ,,
$\frac{1}{2}H_2/H^+$ (at pH = 0)	0.000 ,,
$Ti^{+++} + H_2O/TiO^{++} + 2H^+$ (at pH = 0) .	$+0.04$,,
Sn^{++}/Sn^{++++}	$+0.15$,,
Cu^+/Cu^{++}	$+0.15$,,
$Fe(CN)_6^{----}/Fe(CN)_6^{---}$ . . .	$+0.36$,,
MnO_4^{--}/MnO_4^-	$+0.56$,,
Fe^{++}/Fe^{+++}	$+0.77$,,
$2H_2O/O_2 + 4H^+$ (at pH = 7) . . .	$+0.81$,,
$Mn^{++} = 4H_2O/MnO_4^- + 8H^+$ (at pH = 0) .	$+1.52$ volts
Ce^{+++}/Ce^{++++}	$+1.61$,,
Co^{++}/Co^{+++}	$+1.82$,,

From the values of E^0 we can determine whether a given oxidation-reduction system is capable of oxidizing another.　For instance, if we connect together platinum electrodes dipping respectively into solutions containing ferrous and ferric ions, and cerous and ceric ions, electrons will flow from the electrode at the lower (positive) potential to that at the higher—i.e., from that in the ferrous-ferric solution to that in the cerous-ceric solution.　This means that the following processes will occur :

$$Fe^{++} \rightarrow Fe^{+++} + e, \text{ and } Ce^{++++} + e \rightarrow Ce^{+++}$$

so that the net result is:

$$Fe^{++} + Ce^{++++} \rightarrow Fe^{+++} + Ce^{+++}.$$

In other words, ferrous ions will reduce ceric ions to cerous, being themselves oxidized to ferric ions.　We can, in this way, make the general deduction that a redox system is inherently capable of oxidizing any other redox system with a lower potential.　This is not to say that we can necessarily find the right conditions for such a reaction actually to take place, but it does mean quite definitely that the reverse reaction cannot possibly occur.　All this amounts to saying that the e.m.f. of the cell corresponding to the above reaction gives the affinity of the process—and also indicates the direction in which it can proceed.　In this way, by using a table of standard redox potentials, we can derive a great deal of information about the relative strengths of various oxidizing agents.　The deductions thus made apply strictly only to the cases in which the concentrations of the oxidized and reduced forms in each system are equal, which of course they probably will not be in practice. If, however, we use equation (9), we can derive the correct potentials to be used in each actual situation. As is readily verified, the redox potential is displaced by about 0·06 volts for each ten-fold variation in the ratio [Ox]/[Red]. Thus the conclusions drawn directly from the values of E^0 are relatively seldom invalidated when the actual concentrations are taken into account.

In § 9 we considered the equilibria between metals and solutions of their ions, and showed how electrode potentials arose. Now the process $M \rightarrow M^{++} + 2e$ is, of course, an oxidation reaction, just as much as the process $M^{++} \rightarrow M^{+++} + e$. Thus, electrode potentials are really a special case of the more general oxidation-reduction potentials. Further, equation (9) must hold for the case of a metal in contact with a solution of its ions. The reduced form is now the metal, however, and we must therefore take [Red] as constant. When this constant is absorbed in E^0 we obtain equation (7) of § 9. If we refer back to the table of electrode potentials on p. 74, we may similarly apply the rule that a redox system will be capable of oxidizing another redox system with a lower standard potential. This shows, for instance, that the Ag/Ag$^+$ system, with a standard potential of $+ 0·8$ volt, can oxidize the Zn/Zn^{++} system with a potential of $- 0·76$ volt. In other words, metallic zinc will react with a solution of a silver salt, passing into solution as zinc ions and displacing silver as the metal. The general formulation of this rule will probably be familiar as the statement that a metal can displace from solution all metals coming below it in the electrochemical series. If we include hydrogen, we see that metals coming above hydrogen (with negative potentials) can displace hydrogen from acids, while those metals with positive potentials cannot possibly do so.

When hydrogen ions are concerned in the redox equilibrium, as with potassium permanganate in acid solution (see the table on p. 84), it is clear that the equilibrium position, and hence E^0 for the system, will depend on the pH of the solution. This is also the case for the quinhydrone electrode, which we considered on p. 77.

Finally we may note that just as the pH of a solution can be obtained by finding which indicator the solution causes to change colour, the same sort of thing can be done with so-called redox indicators, which give the redox potential of the solution. These redox indicators are coloured organic substances, which on oxidation or reduction become colourless or are changed into another coloured substance. Of course, the oxidation and reduction of the indicator to the 50 per cent. stage occurs at a definite redox potential (for a given pH) ; from the occurrence or otherwise of the colour change it is possible to find out whether

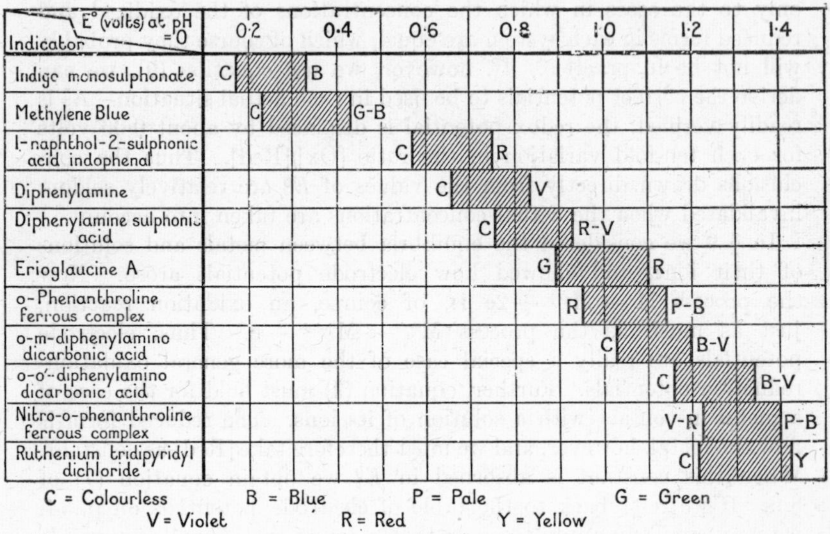

Indicator \ E° (volts) at pH =0	0.2	0.4	0.6	0.8	1.0	1.2	1.4
Indigo monosulphonate	C ▨	B					
Methylene Blue		C ▨ G-B					
1-naphthol-2-sulphonic acid indophenol			C ▨ R				
Diphenylamine				C ▨ V			
Diphenylamine sulphonic acid				C ▨ R-V			
Erioglaucine A					G ▨ R		
o-Phenanthroline ferrous complex					R ▨ P-B		
o-m-diphenylamino dicarbonic acid						C ▨ B-V	
o-o'-diphenylamino dicarbonic acid						C ▨ B-V	
Nitro-o-phenanthroline ferrous complex						V-R ▨ P-B	
Ruthenium tridipyridyl dichloride						C ▨ Y	

C = Colourless   B = Blue   P = Pale   G = Green
V = Violet   R = Red   Y = Yellow

Fig. 28.

the solution under investigation has a higher or lower redox potential than the indicator.

The accompanying graph shows the redox potentials at which eleven redox indicators change colour at pH 0.

14. Solubility Product

This discussion of electrochemistry will conclude with a few remarks on the reason why a solid substance is deposited from a solution of an electrolyte.

In a saturated solution of silver chloride, which will be taken as an example, there is an equilibrium between solid silver chloride, and silver and chloride ions in solution. The rate at which silver and chloride ions pass into solution will be constant at a given temperature, and must at equilibrium be equal to the rate at which silver and chloride ions deposit themselves on the solid crystalline silver chloride. This latter rate—which is therefore constant—is evidently given by the expression $K = [Ag^+][Cl^-]$. This result is a general one for all sparingly soluble electrolytes—that the product of the ionic concentrations is constant for a saturated solution at a given temperature. (Of course, for a compound like Ag_2CrO_4 the expression will be $[Ag^+]^2[CrO_4^{--}]$, and so on). The constant is called the solubility product.

If to a saturated solution of silver chloride (which has a solubility product of about 10^{-10}, and therefore silver and chloride ion concentrations each of about 10^{-5}) we add a solution of potassium chloride, the chloride ion concentration will be very considerably increased.   For the product of the silver and chloride ion concentrations to remain equal to the solubility product, the silver ion concentration will now have to decrease.   That is to say, silver chloride will crystallize out. This phenomenon is essentially the same as that previously dealt with (p. 44) in connection with equilibrium reactions in general.   It will be remembered, however, that the treatment does not hold for concentrated solutions, so that the theory of the solubility product is only of value in connection with very dilute solutions, and therefore for slightly soluble electrolytes.   We shall now consider a few more examples.

If hydrogen sulphide is passed into a solution of copper sulphate, a precipitate of copper sulphide is formed.   This is because cupric sulphide, a very insoluble substance, has an exceedingly small solubility product $[Cu^{++}] [S^{--}]$.   The sulphide ion concentration produced by the dissociation of the hydrogen sulphide (a very weak acid) is not large, but even so the product of the cupric and sulphide ion concentrations would exceed the solubility product of cupric sulphide.   The only way in which this can be avoided is for the cupric ion concentration to become small enough ;   that is, cupric sulphide is precipitated.

If, however, hydrogen sulphide is passed into a solution of nickel sulphate, no nickel sulphide is precipitated ;   the solubility product of nickel sulphide is therefore clearly not reached.   In order to reach it the concentration of sulphide ions must be increased, but if hydrogen sulphide is passed through the solution the solubility of the gas in water at one atmosphere pressure imposes a limit to the sulphide ion concentration that can be reached.

One way of securing a sufficient sulphide ion concentration for the precipitation of nickel sulphide is to use a solution of a soluble sulphide such as ammonium sulphide which, unlike hydrogen sulphide, is completely ionized.

The difference between the metals of the copper/arsenic group in qualitative analysis, and those of the cobalt/manganese group is thus the fact that for the former the solubility product can be reached, but for the latter it cannot be reached with the sulphide ion concentration of a solution saturated with hydrogen sulphide at a pressure of one atmosphere.

We may give yet another application.   If carbon dioxide is passed through a solution of calcium chloride, calcium carbonate is not precipitated.   The reaction

$$CaCl_2 + H_2CO_3 \rightarrow CaCO_3 + 2HCl$$

does not therefore occur in this direction.   If, however, carbon dioxide is passed through lime water, then obviously the solubility product of calcium carbonate is easily reached, because this substance is precipitated :

$$Ca(OH)_2 + H_2CO_3 \rightarrow CaCO_3 + 2H_2O.$$

Why is there this difference ?

In the first reaction the concentration of carbonate ions is clearly insufficient to reach the solubility product of calcium carbonate. This is understandable because carbonic acid is a very weak acid, and a trace of hydrochloric acid formed would markedly depress the dissociation of carbonic acid. The solubility product is therefore not reached owing to lack of carbonate ions. In the case of the second reaction, however, this difficulty does not exist. The hydrogen ions of the carbonic acid and the hydroxyl ions of the hydroxide combine together to give the slightly dissociated water, and the ionization of the carbonic acid is thereby encouraged, giving sufficient carbonate ions to enable the solubility product of calcium carbonate to be reached.

In fact we can say—and the example given will make this clear—that a weak acid is not usually able to displace a stronger acid from its salts.

The reaction

$$MA_{weak} + HA_{strong} \rightleftharpoons MA_{strong} + HA_{weak}$$

where M is a metal ion, A_{weak} is the anion of a weak acid, and A_{strong} is that of a strong acid, thus proceeds predominantly from left to right, except in special cases (like the action of hydrogen sulphide on copper sulphate) where one of the reactants is removed from the equilibrium.

CHAPTER IV

ADSORPTION

1. Henry's Law. The Nernst Distribution Law

If a gas is in contact with a liquid, the liquid will absorb some of the gas. This case is similar to that of the equilibrium of a liquid in contact with its vapour ; at equilibrium the same number of molecules pass in both directions through 1 sq. cm. of the surface in unit time. If, for example, carbon dioxide is in contact with water, equilibrium is reached when as many carbon dioxide molecules dissolve in the water as leave the solution in a given time ; we then have a saturated solution of carbon dioxide.

If the pressure of the carbon dioxide is doubled, the rate at which the carbon dioxide dissolves will also be doubled. Thus, for equilibrium to be maintained, the rate at which carbon dioxide molecules leave the solution must also be doubled, which means that the concentration must be doubled. Thus we have Henry's law, which states : "the solubility of a gas is proportional to its pressure."

Again, if a substance is shaken with two immiscible solvents, in both of which it is soluble, it is found to distribute itself between the two solvents in such a way that the concentrations bear a constant ratio to one another, irrespective of the absolute amount of the substance.

The table below gives the distribution of succinic acid between water and ether at room temperature. c_1 is the concentration in the water layer, c_2 that in the ether. It is seen in the third column that the ratio c_1/c_2 is practically constant.

gm. per litre		$\dfrac{c_1}{c_2}$
in water c_1	in ether c_2	
2·4	0·46	5·2
7·0	1·3	5·2
12·1	2·2	5·4

The relationship can once again be understood from the consideration that equilibrium requires that the same number of molecules per second must pass in the two directions across the interface between the two layers.

G 2

If, however, the substance has different molecular weights in the two media, then the ratio of the concentrations is no longer constant. Let us suppose that the compound exists as single molecules A in the first solvent, and as single molecules in equilibrium with double molecules, $2A \rightleftharpoons A_2$, in the second. The distribution law still holds for the equilibrium of the single molecules A, but not for the measured concentrations of the compound, since the concentration of single molecules in the second solvent is not the same as the total concentration in this solvent. It can, however, be shown that the ratio c_1^2/c_2 should be constant (or $c_1/\sqrt{c_2}$), and this is illustrated by the following figures for benzoic acid distributed between water (c_1) and benzene (c_2), in which it exists partly as double molecules.

c_1	c_2	c_1/c_2	$c_1/\sqrt{c_2}$
1·50	24·2	0·062	0·305
1·90	41·2	0·048	0·304

This is a special case of a more general distribution law which was first deduced by Nernst,

$$\frac{c_1^n}{c_2} = K,$$

where n is the ratio of the molecular weights in the two media.

If the solute undergoes electrolytic dissociation in one medium but not in the other, it is clear that a distribution equilibrium in conformity with Nernst's law holds only for the undissociated molecules, so that $c_1(1 - \alpha)$ is proportional to c_2.

Fig. 29 gives the graphical representation of Henry's law and of the distribution law if the concentrations, c_2, in one solvent are ordinates, and those in the other medium, c_1, are abscissæ. In the case of Henry's law the abscissæ will be gas pressures. Of course, as ordinates we must use c_2, $\sqrt{c_2}$, or $\sqrt[n]{c_2}$, according to the molecular state of the solute in the second medium.

In fact, however, these equations are not obeyed exactly, except in very dilute solutions. Interaction between the solute molecules and between the solute and the solvent can bring about deviations, so that these laws are only true for what are called *ideal* solutions.

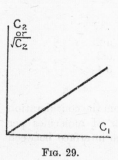

FIG. 29.

In preparative chemistry distribution equilibrium is used to separate one substance, A, from another, B, by adding an immiscible liquid to the mixture in solution. The substance to be separated, A, must be considerably more soluble in the added liquid than is the impurity, B. The liquids are shaken together, when the substance A distributes itself between the two. The liquids are separated and the substance A can be obtained from the added liquid by evaporation. This process is called *extraction*.

2. Adsorption

If a solution of fuchsine, for example, is shaken with animal charcoal, the dissolved dyestuff appears to distribute itself between the liquid and the charcoal. The quantity which is retained by the charcoal appears to depend on the concentration of the fuchsine in the water.

This is a similar process to that dealt with in the preceding paragraph. The carbon plays the part of the ether in the experiment of the last section. The fuchsine, however, instead of dissolving in the bulk of the charcoal is taken up on the surface only ; animal charcoal is an extremely finely divided form of carbon, and therefore has a very large surface for a given volume. Other finely-divided powders possess similar properties. Infusorial earth, powdered bentonite, alumina, and substances which, although compact, have a large internal surface, such as silica gel (see p. 158), are able to take up colouring matters and other substances in the same way as carbon.

We are therefore concerned here with a process which differs from absorption in that it is not a phenomenon in which the volume of the phase determines how much substance is taken up (concentration is always calculated per unit volume), but one in which the available surface is the determining factor. Such a process is called adsorption.

In order to learn more about this process we must get some idea of whether a substance can accumulate in the interface between two phases which are in contact with each other, and if so, how. We must therefore obtain a picture of what takes place in such an interface, which is sometimes called a *capillary layer*.

3. Surface Phenomena

(a) *For a single substance.* It is well known that if a liquid is in contact with its vapour, or with the air, characteristic capillary phenomena come into action at the surface, exemplified for instance by the rise of the liquid in a capillary tube. The surface is the seat of a force, known as surface tension, which amounts, in the case of water, for example, to 72·8 dynes per cm. at 20° C. In other words, 72·8 ergs of work must be done to increase the area of the surface by 1 sq. cm.

For the theory of this phenomenon the reader must consult a textbook of physics. In view of our later discussion a few points must be mentioned here.

If two drops of liquid are brought into contact with each other they coalesce. This can be explained readily enough because the surface is the seat of surface energy (we have just seen that in each square centimetre of the surface of water there are stored about 75 ergs of potential energy).

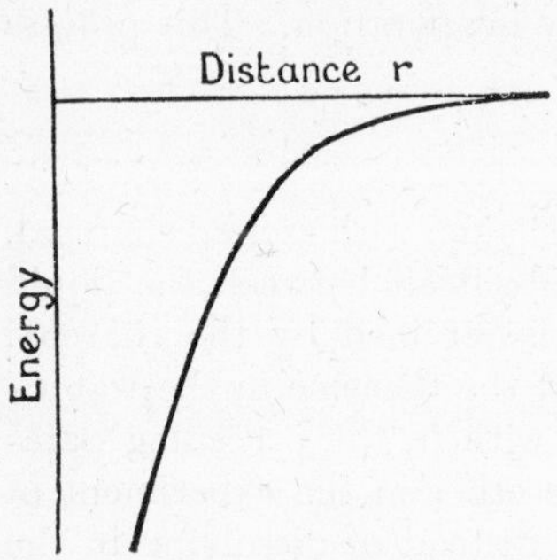

Since the energy tends to become a minimum, the area of the surface will tend to become as small as possible. This can also be expressed by saying that the droplets attract each other ; indeed, in the theory of capillarity it is assumed that all these capillary phenomena owe their origin to the mutual attraction of the molecules—the so-called van der Waals' forces. These forces, however, are effective over only a very small range. Whilst, for example, electrical forces are inversely proportional to the square of the distance (Coulomb's law), van der Waals' forces are inversely proportional to the seventh power of the distance. Larger aggregates of molecules also exert an attraction on each other. We shall return to this fact when we consider colloids (p. 128).

Distance r

Energy

FIG. 30.

In Fig. 30 the abscissæ represent the distance between two molecules or between two aggregates of molecules, and the ordinates represent the potential energy which they have at each particular distance from each other. It will be noted that the attractive force decreases rapidly as the distance increases in agreement with what has just been said (force varies inversely as the seventh power of the distance). Outside a small distance the attraction is virtually zero, but within that distance considerable attractive forces are exerted.

Surface tension can be measured in various ways. Apart from the measurement of the rise of a liquid in a capillary tube, one of the most useful methods of determining the surface tension for a liquid-air surface is by means of a stalagmometer, or drop counter (see Fig. 31). This is a pipette with a characteristic bell-shaped end with an orifice in a plane surface ; the outflowing drops form slowly, so that it is an easy matter to count the number of drops formed as the liquid flows out. The greater the surface tension the larger is the drop before its weight causes it to fall. This method can also be used to measure the interfacial tension between two liquids. If the

FIG. 31.

stalagmometer is filled with water and then placed with the lower end under oil, the interfacial tension between the oil and water (or different solutions) can easily be found by counting the number of drops formed.

The following considerations show that it is also possible to speak of the surface tension of solid substances. It is well known that in an enclosed space small drops distil over on to nearby larger drops. The reason is that the small drops, having a considerably greater surface energy, have a higher vapour pressure than the larger drops. This difference in vapour pressure is thus directly dependent on the existence of a surface energy and therefore of a surface tension. It has been shown in various ways that small crystals have a higher sublimation pressure than large ones, and hence this phenomenon must be associated with surface energy of crystals.

(b) *For solutions*. In any solution, the concentration of the solute in the surface layer is different from that in the bulk of the solution.

Willard Gibbs showed on thermodynamic grounds, that if the dissolved substance lowers the surface tension, the surface layer is richer in that substance than the bulk of the solution itself, and that, conversely, if it raises the surface tension, the surface layer is poorer in this substance than is the bulk of the liquid.

The first case is called positive adsorption, and the second negative adsorption.

Just the same phenomenon occurs at the interface between two liquids, say, at the interface between oil and water. If a substance is dissolved in the water and it lowers the interfacial tension, the substance is more concentrated in the interfacial layer between the oil and the water than in the bulk of the solution. Adsorption phenomena may also occur at the interface between a solid and a liquid, but as it is not possible to measure the surface tension of a solid directly it is not known whether the Gibbs' theory applies in this case, though there is no reason to think the contrary.

4. Adsorption Isotherm

We deal next with the quantitative relationship between the quantity of substance adsorbed and the concentration of the solution. It must be borne in mind that the following treatment holds only for non-electrolytes. When the adsorption of a substance from a solution into the surface layer is investigated the following conclusions are reached. In the first place, the phenomenon is completely reversible ; if a certain quantity of solute is adsorbed from a 0·1 molar solution, then the same quantity is adsorbed no matter how the final concentration of 0·1 molar is arrived at ; in other words the extent of the adsorption is independent of whether a stronger solution is first brought into contact with the adsorbent, and the solution is then diluted with water, or a weaker solution is first used and the final state is reached by the addition of a stronger one. Adsorption is thus a reversible equilibrium phenomenon.

In the second place we may investigate the connection between the amount of substance adsorbed per square centimetre of surface and the concentration of the solution. If an adsorbent such as powdered charcoal is used it is exceedingly difficult to determine the extent of the carbon-liquid surface. Since, however, adsorption is entirely a surface process, the adsorption can be characterized by the total adsorbed mass, x, divided by the total surface. Difficulties arising in this case may be avoided as follows : for a given sample of charcoal, the total surface of 2 gm. of the powder will undoubtedly be twice as great as that of 1 gm. Instead of dividing by the surface area, the mass adsorbed by 1 gm. of carbon is calculated. This method can only be used, of course, so long as results obtained from one and the same specimen of carbon are under consideration.

The mass of substance adsorbed is connected with the concentration of the solution by the equation

$$\frac{x}{m} = kc^{\frac{1}{n}}$$

where m is the mass of the adsorbent, and k and n are constants which have different values for each solute and adsorbent, and c is the concentration of the substance after the adsorption equilibrium has been reached. $\frac{1}{n}$ usually has a value lying between 0·2 and 0·7.

Fig. 32 shows graphically the connection between the mass adsorbed per gram of carbon and the equilibrium concentration of the solution. If we look at this curve, which is called the adsorption isotherm (because the curve changes with temperature, but is fixed for one given

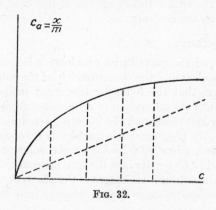

Fig. 32.

temperature), it is seen at once that the rate of increase of x/m with c is greatest where the concentration of the solute is least, and falls off at the higher values of the concentration. Hence the process of adsorption is relatively more important with the more dilute solutions. If the mass adsorbed per unit mass of the adsorbent is called c_a, then if the solute were to be distributed according to the Nernst law, we should have $c_a = kc$. This equation is represented by the dotted line in Fig. 32 (compare Fig. 29, p. 90), while for the actual adsorption the equation is

$$c_a = k_1 c^{\frac{1}{n}}.$$

This is what gives rise to the characteristic form of the adsorption isotherm and the fact that the effect is relatively larger at small concentrations. If we put $\dfrac{1}{n} = \dfrac{1}{2}$, the adsorption isotherm becomes

$c_a = kc^{\frac{1}{2}}$. Suppose we are dealing with sugar molecules, which dissolve as single molecules in water, then this equation, regarded as an expression of the Nernst distribution law, would mean that the sugar is present in the carbon in the form of molecules half as large as those present in the aqueous solution, which, of course, is absurd. The adsorption isotherm is, therefore, connected with a phenomenon which is essentially different from that governed by the Nernst distribution law.

If we take logarithms of both sides of the equation $\dfrac{x}{m} = kc^{\frac{1}{n}}$ we get

$$\log \frac{x}{m} = \log k + \frac{1}{n}\log c.$$

If, now, we plot $\log \dfrac{x}{m}$ against $\log c$ we should get a straight line, because this is an equation of the first degree. The logarithmic adsorption isotherm is thus a straight line.

The above expression for the adsorption isotherm which is usually known as the Freundlich adsorption isotherm, has no theoretical basis, but is based simply on observed facts. We have seen from Gibbs' theory that there is a connection between the lowering of the surface tension of a liquid by a solute, and the adsorption of the solute in the surface layer. It is therefore reasonable to expect that the lowering of the surface tension will be connected with the concentration of the solution in the same way as the mass adsorbed by a solid adsorbent is connected with the concentration ; and, in fact, it has been shown that the lowering of the surface tension of water by dissolution of a substance in it is connected with the concentration of the solute by the equation

$$\Delta\sigma = qc^{\frac{1}{n}}$$

where $\Delta\sigma$ is the lowering of the surface tension, and q and $\dfrac{1}{n}$ are constants. The lower the surface tension of the solute added, the more the curve giving the relation between surface tension and concentration deviates more from the straight line (see Fig. 33).

Adsorption equilibria are attained quickly. If equilibrium has not been reached in about twenty minutes, then some effect other than adsorption of the type we have been discussing is probably coming into play. The effect of temperature on the adsorption is usually small.

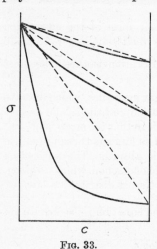

σ

c

FIG. 33.

There is another adsorption formula which also expresses the experimental data satisfactorily. It is called Langmuir's formula,

$$\frac{x}{m} = \frac{k_1 c}{1 + k_2 c}$$

where k_1 and k_2 are constants, which have different values for each solute and for each medium. The symbols x, m, and c have the same significance as in the Freundlich isotherm. Langmuir's formula has a better theoretical basis than that of Freundlich.

Let us suppose that for 1 sq. cm. of a given surface there are N available places for adsorption. At equilibrium suppose that n of them are occupied ; there will thus be $(N - n)$ free places. The rate of adsorption is just equal to the rate of desorption, at equilibrium. But the rate of adsorption is proportional to the concentration of the solute and to the number of free places—that is, rate of adsorption $= k_a(N - n)c$. On the other hand, the rate of desorption depends only on the number of occupied places—that is, rate of desorption $= k_d n$. Thus, at equilibrium

$$k_a(N - n)c = k_d n$$

and

$$n = \frac{k_a N c}{(k_d + k_a c)} = \frac{k_1 c}{(1 + k_2 c)}$$

where $\qquad k_1 = k_a N / k_d$, and $k_2 = k_a / k_d$.

But x/m is directly proportional to the number of occupied places, n per sq. cm. Hence Langmuir's adsorption isotherm follows.

An important difference between the two is that Langmuir's formula takes account of the fact that for very large values of c the surface becomes saturated, and can take up no more. For large values of c, k_2c greatly exceeds 1, so the latter can be neglected and the equation then becomes

$$\frac{x}{m} = \frac{k_1}{k_2},$$

that is, the mass of the substance adsorbed reaches a constant value which is not exceeded although c may be increased. Also for small values of c, k_2c may be neglected in comparison with unity. The equation then becomes

$$\frac{x}{m} = k_1c,$$

showing that the amount adsorbed is proportional to the concentration when the surface is nearly bare.

The ease with which different molecules are adsorbed varies widely. Broadly speaking, large molecules are more readily adsorbed than small ones, and aromatic molecules than aliphatic. Also, the presence of hydroxyl, carbonyl, amino and similar groups makes for increased ease of adsorption. For related series of compounds the adsorption increases with increasing molecular weight.

It is obvious that the process of adsorption with its characteristic increase of concentration locally in the boundary layer must play a part in those processes where very small quantities of substances exert a great effect. We refer to catalytic actions, the effect of enzymes, antiseptics, and toxicological and pharmacological agents. In all these processes there is a large effect brought about by very dilute solutions, but it is very probable that although the solutions themselves may be very dilute, higher concentrations will exist locally in the boundary layer due to adsorption.

Adsorption is determined simply by adding a weighed amount of the adsorbent (for example, powdered charcoal) to a solution of known concentration. After the adsorption equilibrium has been attained, the powdered charcoal is separated from the liquid by centrifuging or filtration (correction may have to be made for adsorption on the filter paper). The concentration of solute remaining in the separated liquid is determined, and from this the mass of substance adsorbed per gram of adsorbent is calculated.

The simultaneous adsorption of two solutes is as yet little understood, but as far as the present state of our knowledge goes it is clear that each of the two solutes is generally adsorbed from the mixture less strongly than it would be if the other solute were not present. This may be due to competition for the available space on the surface. A substance which is strongly adsorbed appears to exert a repressing effect on the adsorption of one which by itself is more weakly adsorbed. Since the adsorption equilibrium is a dynamic one, it may well be that a second substance will displace some of the first substance from the surface, even if it is added after equilibrium has been reached for the first substance.

For instance, in an actual experiment 3 gm. of charcoal were added to a solution containing 9 gm. of glucose per litre, whereby almost 4 gm. per litre of the glucose were withdrawn. 0·07 gm.-mol. of *iso*butyl-urethane was then added to the liquid. This substance was strongly adsorbed, and only 0·2 gm. of glucose was retained by the carbon.

What has taken place here is unmistakably a kind of poisoning ; in the presence of the urethane, the other substance can no longer occur to any extent in the boundary layer. This gives an idea of how a very small quantity of a foreign substance can act as a biological poison by preventing access of some compound to the surface of a particular enzyme, and thus interfering with an essential metabolic process.

5. Chromatography

Adsorption has many applications in preparative chemistry. In order to remove colouring matters from all kinds of solutions activated charcoal is added. This strongly adsorbs dyes. Gases and liquids can be dried by adsorbing the water from them on finely divided silica in the form of silica gel.

A much used application of adsorption is to be found in chromatography. This method, which was discovered by the botanist Tswett in 1903, passed unnoticed until recent years when it was revived. It is now an extremely important method of separating substances. Tswett passed an extract of plant colouring matters in ligroin over a column of finely divided calcium carbonate, and then washed the column with pure ligroin. The colouring matters remained adsorbed on the calcium carbonate and were " fixed " in the upper part of the column. By washing, the colouring matters dissolve, but they are adsorbed again lower down the column. The stronger the substance is adsorbed (i.e. the smaller the concentration of the dye in the liquid) the slower is the dye moved down the column, so that definite coloured rings are formed at different levels in the column depending on the strength of the adsorption. This is shown in Fig. 34. In

Fig. 34. this way Tswett discovered that there were two types of chlorophyll in certain carotenoids. By sufficiently long washing the rings can be driven one by one from the column.

Since, as we have just seen, the most strongly adsorbed substance has the smallest concentration in the liquid, it is often difficult to obtain well-defined rings with the last remaining adsorbate, which tends to form a tail. This does not happen when the concentration is directly proportional to the adsorption, as for the distribution between two liquids. This suggested the idea of distribution chromatography, in which one of the two liquids is held by the column in the pores of a finely divided substance, while the other is passed over it. A simple form of this is paper chromatography. In this method a strip of filter paper soaked in water is used as the column. The chromatogram is developed with a liquid, such as butanol, phenol, etc., which is immiscible with water. It is not difficult with this technique to separate the mixtures of amino-acids obtained by the hydrolysis of proteins, and even to determine them quantitatively ; before the advent of chromatography this was a very difficult thing to do.

Chromatography may be used not only with coloured substances but also with colourless ones. The adsorbed substance can be made visible by its fluorescence in ultra-violet light, by chemical colour reactions, or even by changes in the refractive index of the washing liquid.

6. Adsorption of Electrolytes

Adsorption from solutions of electrolytes is more complicated, since solid adsorbents may have an adsorbed layer of ions before being placed in the solution. What then takes place is a kind of exchange adsorption between the ions in solution and those already on the surface. The Freundlich and Langmuir isotherms do not usually apply in this case.

Van Bemmelen carried out a classical experiment in which he showed that certain preparations of manganese dioxide adsorbed potassium chloride, in such a way that the solution remaining after the adsorption had an acid reaction. At first sight it might be supposed that hydrolysis of the potassium chloride had taken place. The explanation is, however, different. The manganese dioxide was prepared from potassium permanganate and sulphuric acid. In the preparation the manganese dioxide had already adsorbed sulphuric acid. When the manganese dioxide prepared in this manner was added to a solution of potassium chloride, potassium ions were adsorbed, and an equivalent quantity of hydrogen ions, arising from the adsorbed sulphuric acid, was set free. On this account the liquid reacted acid after the adsorption.

The sulphuric acid was thus adsorbed on the manganese dioxide originally in such a way that the hydrogen ions were readily exchanged for other cations. The sulphate ion must therefore be strongly held, and the hydrogen ion less strongly. The situation arising is shown in Fig. 35. We clearly have an electrical double layer at the surface of the manganese dioxide particles. We have met with a similar state

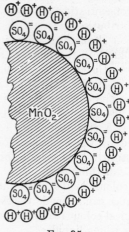

of affairs on p. 71 (see Fig. 22 on that page). Such an electrical double layer is the seat of an electrical potential difference. In the following chapter we shall see to what electrical phenomena such a double layer can give rise.

The inner part of the double layer is not always formed by the adsorbed ions themselves. Suppose, for example, that we have stannic oxide, SnO_2, particles in place of manganese dioxide. No double layer appears to be formed in pure water, but if a little potassium hydroxide is added to the water a double layer is at once produced. We shall see on p. 134 that the caustic potash reacts with the outermost layer of the stannic oxide particles to give potassium stannate, K_2SnO_3. The inner

FIG. 35.

part of the double layer now consists of stannate ions, SnO_3^{--}, and potassium, K^+, ions in the liquid form the opposite side of the layer.

Clay and its exchange with substances dissolved in water in the soil gives another example of exchange adsorption. The clay particles are silicates ; (complex) silicic acid ions form the inner side of the double layer, whilst Ca^{++}, Na^+, H^+ and other ions form the opposite side. The extent of the exchange depends on the nature of the soil liquid. The latter can often be affected by the addition of artificial manures to the ground.

The following treatment gives an insight of a quantitative kind into the process of exchange adsorption.

We will take as an example a silver iodide powder on which potassium iodide is adsorbed (this example is dealt with more fully on p. 136). The iodide ions are strongly adsorbed by the silver iodide, and the potassium ions form the outer layer of the double layer. What will happen when the substance is added to a solution of nitric acid ? Some of the hydrogen ions of the acid solution will change places with the potassium ions.

Consider unit area of the silver iodide surface (suppose we choose the surface of 1 gm. of the silver iodide powder) upon which a iodide ions are situated. Originally there would also have been a potassium ions opposite the iodide ions, but now, assuming equilibrium to have been reached, there will be n_1 hydrogen ions and n_2 potassium ions, so that $n_1 + n_2 = a$. The fact that there is equilibrium means that as many hydrogen ions leave the solution and enter the adsorption layer as leave it in a given time (and the same, of course, for the potassium ions). The number of ions leaving the solution will be proportional to the concentrations of hydrogen and potassium ions, respectively, in the solution. Thus

$$\frac{n_1}{n_2} = K \frac{c_1}{c_2},$$

or, since $a = n_1 + n_2$

$$\frac{n_1}{a - n_1} = K \frac{c_1}{c_2}.$$

This formula can be written in terms of gram-molecules by dividing n_1 and $a - n_1$ by N (Avogadro's number, see p. 5). Let $\frac{n_1}{N}$ be x_1, and let $\frac{a}{N}$ be X. Then

$$\frac{x_1}{X - x_1} = K \frac{c_1}{c_2}.$$

X is thus the maximum number of gram-cations that can be exchanged, and may be called the exchange capacity of the adsorbent.

It will now be clear how this exchange adsorption differs from ordinary adsorption. The quantity of hydrogen ions, x_1, retained by the exchange adsorbent does not depend on the concentration of these ions in the solution, c_1, but on the ratio c_1/c_2. Addition of water (which, of course, does not change the ratio of concentrations) is thus without effect on the adsorption.

We may note the following points about the value of the constant K in the above formula. If the adsorbent shows no preference for one or other of the two ions, this constant is equal to unity. Some adsorbents, of course, show a decided preference. For clay, for example, the preference for exchange of alkali metal ions is according to the following " permutit " series : *

$$Li < Na < K < Rb < Cs < H$$

and the K values increase in the same order.

The reader should note carefully that the above treatment holds only for ions of the same valency. If this is not the case the relationship becomes more complicated, and we shall not enter into the matter more fully here. Synthetic ion exchange resins with a large exchange capacity have been commercially available for the last ten years or so.

---

* Permute = exchange ; the permutites are silicates which are used industrially for the softening of water (i.e., exchange of Ca^{++} ions for Na^{+} ions).

Both cation and anion exchange resins are made. They are frequently used in chromatographic separations.

7. Structure of the Interfacial Layer according to Langmuir and Harkins

If the electrical double layer at the surface of a particle is brought about by adsorption from an electrolyte, the question arises why the adsorbed electrolyte orients itself in such a way that a double layer is produced. The reason might be that one of the ions of the electrolyte fits particularly well into the crystal lattice of the adsorbent. This applies, for example, to the adsorption of potassium iodide on silver iodide where the iodide ions form the inner part of the double layer. Another reason might be that one of the two ions belongs to a class of substance which is strongly adsorbed. In the soaps, for example, one ion is small and inorganic ; the other is large and organic. The organic ion forms the inner side of the layer. Investigations of Langmuir and Harkins have given some explanation of the phenomena which lie behind the process. These investigators, have shown that in general, large organic ions and organic molecules which are not ionized but have a polar group do not lie at random on a surface, but are orientated in a definite direction. Langmuir determined the area occupied by a layer of fatty acid molecules spread on the surface of water. A given mass of a fatty acid, dissolved in benzene, was added to water ; the benzene evaporated and the fatty acid spread itself over the surface of the water. The fatty acid film was now confined between two glass barriers, one of which was fitted with a torsion arrangement for measuring the force exerted on it by the film. The barriers were moved so as gradually to decrease the area of the film, and by observing the way in which the force increased, it was possible to determine the area at which the molecules of the fatty acid were just in contact, forming a monomolecular layer. In this way, from a knowledge of Avogadro's number, the area occupied in the surface by one molecule could be found. Further, the length of each molecule could be derived by dividing the total volume of the fatty acid by the area of the film. If the molecules were arranged at random, the length of the molecule and the diameter of the cross-section would have the same mean value. Actually, according to the determinations of Langmuir, this is by no means the case. The fatty acid molecules have a length which exceeds the diameter many times. This is completely in agreement with the view that in the fatty acid molecule there is a long chain of CH_2 groups with a terminal —COOH group. Obviously the molecules are so oriented that the —COOH group is situated in the water, while the hydrocarbon chain sticks out from it. Length and cross-section of fatty acid molecules as determined by spreading experiments, agree well with dimensions determined by other means, e.g. by X-ray diffraction.

Harkins came to the same conclusion by a totally different method. He deduced from measurements of interfacial tensions that at the interface between *iso*amyl alcohol and water, for example, the molecules of the alcohol are so directed that the hydroxyl groups are attracted into the water and the hydrocarbon chain into the alcohol. In general the polar part of the molecule is always directed towards the water. By the polar part of a molecule is meant that region where there is some local separation of charge. For instance, the carbonyl group is a polar group, because the electrons of the double bond are more attracted to the oxygen atom than to the carbon, and the carbon and oxygen atoms thus acquire fractional positive and negative charges. The hydroxyl, amino and nitro groups are other examples of polar groups.

The observations of Langmuir and Harkins apply especially to molecules with a polar " head " (such as the carboxyl group) and a non-polar " tail " (such as a hydrocarbon chain). They are called amphipolar substances. When the two ends of the molecule are more alike, oriented adsorption becomes less important. However, the typical example of the fatty acid gives a clear picture of the adsorption of an electrolyte giving rise to an electrical double layer because the electrolyte is oriented on the boundary surface. This explains how it comes about that the particle on which the electrolyte is adsorbed has an electrical charge opposite to that of the immediately surrounding liquid.

CHAPTER V

ELECTRO-KINETIC PHENOMENA

1. The Importance of Electro-kinetic Phenomena

In a later chapter we shall deal more fully with colloids. We shall then learn that a colloidal solution consists of very finely divided material suspended in water or some other medium and that these particles carry an electric charge. The charge is closely connected with the most important properties of colloidal systems (see p. 127).

In § 6 and § 7 of the previous chapter we saw that electrolytes can give rise to an electrical double layer at the surface of particles. Direct measurement of the potential difference of the double layer at the surface of a non-metal is not so easy to carry out as for the double layer between a metal and a solution of an electrolyte. Yet we can arrive at a picture of the electrical condition of such a non-metallic surface from a group of electro-kinetic phenomena.

Four phenomena belong to this group :

1. *Electro-endosmosis* or electro-osmosis : where a liquid moves with respect to a surface under the influence of an applied potential difference.

2. *Electrophoresis* : where a particle moves with respect to a liquid on account of an applied potential difference.

3. *Streaming potential* : where a potential difference is set up in consequence of the movement of a liquid with respect to a surface.

4. *Sedimentation-* and *centrifugation-potential* : where a potential difference is set up in consequence of the movement of particles in a liquid. The movement is caused by gravity (sedimentation) or more strongly by a centrifugal field.

The electro-kinetic phenomena are complementary in pairs. An applied electric field causes motion in the case of electro-endosmosis and electrophoresis. Movement causes a potential difference in the case of streaming potential and sedimentation potential. Since sedimentation- and centrifugation-potentials have rarely been investigated, we shall limit our discussion to the first three phenomena.

2. Electro-endosmosis

Fig. 36 represents a porous pot provided with a vertical tube. The porous pot is placed in water, and there is an electrode inside the pot (which also contains water) and one outside. If a potential

difference is applied to the two electrodes so that the electrode inside
the pot is negative, then, in consequence of the potential difference,
there is a flow of liquid through the porous walls and hence a rise of
liquid in the vertical tube. It is to be noted that we are dealing here
with a porous pot, *not* with a semi-permeable membrane. The capillaries in the porous pot are concerned with
the phenomenon, which in this form bears a
superficial resemblance to osmosis (hence the
name, electro-endosmosis), although, in fact,
it has nothing in common with it.

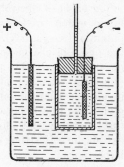

The phenomenon may be considered
simply, as follows : Fig. 37 represents a single
capillary tube with an electrode at each end.
What actually occurs is that the liquid, in
consequence of the applied potential difference, flows through the capillary from left
to right if E_1 is the positive and E_2 the negative electrode.

FIG. 36.

Since the liquid itself moves with respect to
the walls in the direction of the negative electrode, it must carry a
positive charge. The capillary, together with its contents, must be
electrically neutral ; consequently the capillary wall carries a negative
charge. On the basis of the discussion of the previous chapter we may
take it that the molecules are adsorbed in such a way that the ions are

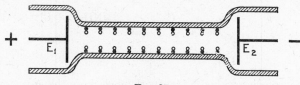

FIG. 37.

arranged in an electrical double layer. What ions actually constitute
this double layer we shall leave for the time being. For convenience we
can assume that they arise from the water, and that negatively charged
hydroxyl ions are held fast by the solid wall, whilst positively charged
hydrogen ions are in the movable liquid.

It has been shown that the direction of flow of the liquid depends
on the nature of the wall. Instead of using a porous wall through
which the water streamed, the water was made to pass through a
plug held in a tube. If this plug was made of sulphur, silicates, or
glass wool, the walls of the capillaries in the plugs became negatively
charged and the liquid positively charged, and the liquid therefore
flowed to the cathode. If, on the other hand, the plug was made of a

substance such as alumina, the water was negatively charged, and the surface positively. This is easy to explain. The alumina, Al_2O_3, acts, in contact with water, as a base, $Al(OH)_3$; the double layer will thus be built up so that the Al^{+++} ions remain on the wall of the plug, and the OH^- ions are in the adjacent liquid, which is thus negatively charged.

The effect of electrolytes can be studied by measuring the volume of liquid which traverses a capillary in unit time for a given applied potential (see Fig. 37). The effective ion is then found to be that with the opposite charge to that of the wall. If, for example, the wall is negatively charged, a potassium salt, giving rise to positively charged potassium ions, K^+, slows down the endosmosis, a barium salt, with its double charged ion, Ba^{++}, is more effective, an aluminium salt giving rise to a triply charged ion, Al^{+++}, is more effective still, and a thorium salt with its fourfold positively charged ion, Th^{++++}, exerts an extraordinarily strong effect. The valency of the anion is of subsidiary importance.

This rule for the connection between the effect on the electro-kinetic process and the valency of the oppositely charged ion holds only for the ordinary inorganic ions, such as K, Na, Mg, Zn, CO_3, NO_3, Cl, SO_4, etc. Organic ions seem to be more active than their valency would lead one to expect, so that, for example, an organic dyestuff, such as fuchsine,

decreases the electro-kinetic transport much more than an equivalent quantity of potassium chloride, in spite of the fact that the ions are both univalent. Moreover, the ions of the heavy metals are also more active than would be expected from their valency. This is also the order of the ease of adsorption, so that adsorption is plainly responsible for the effect just discussed.

When it is remembered that experiment has shown that organic substances are more strongly adsorbed than inorganic (p. 97) and that heavy metals are more strongly adsorbed than light ones, it might be thought that adsorption plays some part in the process of electro-endosmosis. This will be taken up again in § 6 of this chapter.

A very special part appears to be played by those ions which are present both in the solution and also in the solid wall or have a close relationship to the material of which the wall is composed. Hydroxyl ions, for example, increase electro-endosmosis in a glass capillary, and bromide ions increase it when a silver bromide surface is used. We shall return to this point on p. 114.

3. Streaming Potentials

If, in an apparatus such as that shown in Fig. 36, liquid is forced down the vertical tube into the porous pot and through its pores, a potential difference is set up between the two electrodes. As before, this phenomenon is more readily understood when only a single capillary is considered, as shown in Fig. 37. If liquid is forced through the capillary, a potential difference is set up between the electrodes.

This can be tested practically by a method such as that indicated

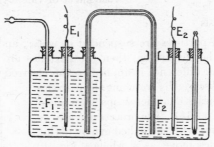

FIG. 38.

in Fig. 38. By means of compressed air, the liquid is forced from the Woulff's bottle, F_1, through the capillary into the bottle, F_2. The two electrodes, E_1 and E_2, serve for the measurement of the streaming potential produced. Streaming potentials have their origin again in an electrical double layer which exists between the glass of the capillary and the liquid. If the liquid is forced from one bottle to the other it carries the positive charge with it, making the electrode in F_2 positive and that in F_1 negative. Of course, the potential difference between the two electrodes arising in this manner at the same time gives rise to an electrical transport in the opposite direction. The degree of this transport depends on the conductivity of the system. It is possible to calculate from the experimentally determined streaming potential the value of the potential drop, ζ, across the double layer. Helmholtz deduced the expression

$$\zeta = \frac{4\pi\eta}{D} \cdot K \cdot \frac{E}{P}$$

where D is the dielectric constant, η the viscosity, K the specific conductivity of the system, P the applied pressure, and E the measured streaming potential.

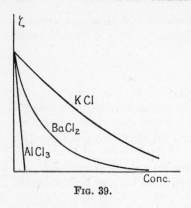

FIG. 39.

Investigations of the streaming potential, especially those concerned with the effect of electrolytes on the potential, have given results which agree with those on endosmosis. The depressing effect of cations (which carry a charge opposite to that of the glass capillary) is again governed by the valency, and once more organic ions and ions of heavy metals have been found to occupy anomalous positions. Fig. 39 gives an idea of the effect of valency.

4. Electrophoresis

If very small particles are suspended in water, and two electrodes are placed in the suspension, then the particles are found to move when a potential difference is applied to the electrodes. This pheno- menon can be observed by watching the particles themselves by means of a microscope or an ultra- microscope (see p. 118). The process can also be seen to take place with the naked eye by noting how the particles move as a whole. Fig. 40 shows the apparatus by which electrophoresis can be demonstrated by the latter method. The U-tube contains the suspension to be investi- gated, and is so arranged that there is a layer of clear liquid in each of the limbs above the coloured suspension. Two electrodes are placed in the liquid, and a potential difference is applied to the two electrodes. The suspension is found to move round to one limb. This can be followed by observing the movement of the boundary between the water and the suspension.

The Swedish scientist Tiselius has developed a very much better apparatus for measuring electrophoresis. It is shown diagrammatically in Fig. 41.

The U-tube is not circular in cross-section, but rectangular. This promotes cooling and has, moreover, optical advantages. The U-tube con- sists of a number of sections, each of which fits into the next. In the diagram the lowest two are filled with the suspension, and above them

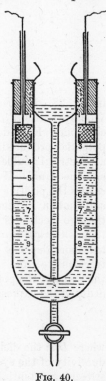

FIG. 40.

is the clear liquid, which also fills the electrode vessels. The apparatus is completely immersed in a thermostat, and the different sections of the U-tube are then displaced so as to bring them into line. Sharp boundaries are thus obtained between the suspension and the clear liquid.

The electrodes are Ag-AgCl electrodes immersed in a concentrated solution of potassium chloride in order to avoid the evolution of gas.

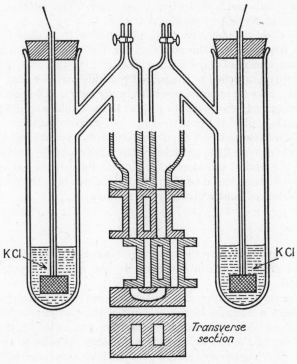

KCl   KCl

Transverse section

FIG. 41.

The electrode vessels are large enough to enable the electrophoresis to go on for a sufficient time before products of electrolysis reach the U-tube. The electrode vessels are connected to the U-tube by rubber or plastic tubing.

Experiments with the Tiselius apparatus are usually carried out at about 2–4° C. as in this temperature range the density of water is least dependent upon temperature and consequently convection is slight.

The method is so refined that by means of electrophoresis experiments on serum, four different protein components have been discovered, each moving with a different speed. Not only has the speed been determined, but also the quantity of each present. The motion of the boundary is observed by noting changes of refractive index.

A still more recent and very simple form of electrophoresis experiment is paper electrophoresis. A long strip of filter paper is dipped into a solution and at one place a small amount of the suspension is added. If the paper is now placed in an electric field the suspended particles move, and if they are not all identical they move with different speeds and a separation takes place. This method, again, is used particularly in protein chemistry.

The cause of the phenomenon can be ascribed to an electrical double layer at the surface of the particles. If, for example, we are dealing with a suspension of ferric hydroxide, $Fe(OH)_3$, in water, ferric ions, Fe^{+++}, remain attached to the ferric hydroxide particles, and hydroxyl ions, OH^-, take up opposite positions in the liquid. The particles thus become positively charged with respect to the liquid, and if a potential difference is applied the positively charged particles will move towards the negative electrode. Various investigators have studied the effect on the movement of the particles of the addition of electrolytes to the liquid. Theoretical considerations have shown that the velocity, u, of a particle is proportional to the potential difference in the double layer of the particle, ζ, and is given by the formula

$$u = \frac{HD}{4\eta\pi}\zeta$$

where the symbols have the same significance as on p. 107. H is the potential gradient, or, in other words, the change of potential per centimetre.

In the case of electrophoresis too, it appears that electrolytes usually bring about a decrease in the velocity of the particles under a given potential gradient. The extent of this decrease, as before, depends on the valency of the ion which carries a charge opposite to that of the particle. For negatively charged gold particles, suspended in water, for example, the univalent potassium ion, K^+, exerts a weak retarding effect, the divalent barium ion, Ba^{++}, a stronger one, and the trivalent aluminium ion, Al^{+++}, a stronger effect still if salts containing these ions are dissolved in the same equivalent concentrations. Fig. 42 illustrates this point. The electrophoretic velocity, u, or the quantity ζ may be taken as ordinates (ζ being directly proportional to u, as the above equation indicates). Concentrations, expressed in equivalents, are the abscissæ. The curve marked $+$ is that for a univalent cation, and that marked $++$ is the curve for a divalent cation, etc. The ions with the same charge as the particle, i.e., the anions of the above salts, exert a much smaller effect on the gold particles. Thus, the curves for

potassium chloride, nitrate, and sulphate, are almost identical, and fall
practically on the curve marked + in the figure.

If, on the other hand, the particles have a positive charge (as in the
case of ferric and other hydroxides), the valency of the anion governs
the velocity of electrophoresis. A univalent anion, such as the nitrate
ion, NO_3^-, has a weak retarding effect, the divalent sulphate ion,
SO_4^{--}, a stronger one, and the phosphate ion, PO_4^{---}, which has a
charge of three units, has a stronger effect still. In this case the
cation plays a subsidiary part. The curve with one positive sign (+)
represents equally well the effects of potassium nitrate, KNO_3, and of
barium nitrate, $Ba(NO_3)_2$ (or rather $\frac{1}{2}Ba(NO_3)_2$, as equivalent

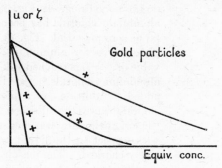

FIG. 42.

concentrations of NO_3^- must be compared) on the velocity of the
hydroxide particles.

There is still, however, much to be explained in connection with
these electrophoresis phenomena. An exceptional part is played by
those ions which are closely related to the crystal lattice of the particles
themselves. As an example we may take particles of silver iodide
suspended in water. Addition of iodide ions (by dissolving potassium
iodide in the water) increases the electrophoretic velocity, and therefore
the potential, ζ; silver ions, Ag^+, on the other hand, exert a particularly
strong retarding effect. The same phenomenon is shown in the case
of positively charged ferric hydroxide particles, $Fe(OH)_3$. Addition of
hydrogen ions (acid) increases, whilst addition of hydroxyl ions
decreases the electrophoretic velocity.

On pp. 114 and 115 we shall consider the effect of these ions further,
but the above statements make it clear that the *common ions* (i.e.
ions similar in nature to the particles themselves) play a different part
from other ions (often called *indifferent ions*). We shall consider the
electrophoresis of proteins on p. 141ff.

5. Reversal of Sign of the Potential

We saw in the preceding paragraph that one common ion raises the potential, whilst the other, on the contrary, lowers it. This may go so far as to reverse the sign of the charge. If to a suspension of silver iodide particles increasing amounts of silver nitrate are added, there is first a fall in ϵ, and therefore a fall in ζ. ζ becomes zero, then the electrophoresis reverses its direction, the now positive potential difference gradually increasing with increasing silver ion concentration. The " common " ion can thus bring about a reversal of sign.

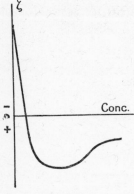

FIG. 43.

Some indifferent ions, however, appear to do the same thing. In Fig. 39 the curve for aluminium chloride has been given only as far as zero potential. Fig. 43 gives the complete curve for aluminium chloride ; the value of $\zeta = 0$ is reached when $0 \cdot 8$ μ-mol. of aluminium chloride * per litre has been added. Addition of more aluminium chloride causes the adsorbed layer, which in the original state was negatively charged with respect to the liquid, to become positively charged. The reason is to be found in the fact that aluminium hydroxide, $Al(OH)_3$, is formed by hydrolysis. This is positively charged, so that the wall of the tube, which is covered with a very thin layer of it, also shows a positive ζ-potential with respect to the liquid.

It is obvious that this cannot go on to an unlimited extent ; the negatively charged chloride ions prevent the potential from becoming too positive. The positive potential therefore only rises to a maximum, and then begins to fall again.

The extent to which the hydrolysis of a salt takes place depends on the pH. The reader should turn to p. 65, equation (3). Addition of hydrogen ions, H^+, causes a decrease of the hydroxyl ion concentration, OH^-, so that decrease of pH opposes hydrolysis. Addition of acid thus opposes the reversal of sign of the ζ-potential, and addition of alkali favours it.

6. Further Explanation of this Phenomenon

How can we explain the fact that indifferent electrolytes exert such a large influence on electokinetic phenomena ? In order to understand the effect of electrolytes we must first have a clear picture of the

* 1 μ-mol. $= 10^{-6}$ gm.-mol.

electrical double layer and of the potential which is at the foundation of electrokinetic processes.

We have seen that the origin of electrokinetic phenomena is to be found in the double layer, which consists of ions adsorbed on the surface of the particles and of their opposite or counter-ions. The first are held fast on the surface, the second are attracted towards the surface ions by electrostatic forces. If they were not attracted they would, of course, diffuse away. They are thus submitted to two effects, one which keeps them near the surface (the electrical attraction of the surface ions), and the other which tends to make them move away (the tendency to diffusion, which was dealt with in Chapter I, and is a consequence of thermal motion). A similar phenomenon will be familiar from elemen-

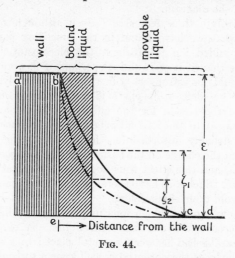

Fig. 44.

tary science. Air molecules are attracted towards the earth (by the force of gravity), but tend, through thermal agitation, to diffuse away into space. The consequence is that our terrestrial atmosphere has a density decreasing with height. It is just the same with the counter ions ; they will be distributed " atmospherically," being densest near the surface, and gradually thinning out at greater distances from it.

In Fig. 44 the potential difference between the surface and the bulk of the liquid is represented by the distance ϵ. The two curves give the potential at various distances from the surface, these distances being abscissæ on the graph. The gradual decrease of potential with distance shown by the curves is due to the gradual thinning out of the ionic atmosphere. We cannot measure the total potential difference electro-kinetically, for some liquid (shown by the area hatched by sloping lines) remains attached to the surface and does not move with the rest. The effective electro-kinetic potential is therefore ζ_1 or ζ_2. The broken curve has a steeper slope than the full curve and hence a sharper decrease with distance in the density of the ionic atmosphere and a smaller value of ζ. What determines the slope of the potential curve ?

Let us consider a surface washed with water. Suppose the full line holds for this case. Now suppose an electrolyte is dissolved in the water, the electrolyte dissociating into anions and cations. The cations of the electrolyte can function as opposing ions just as well as those already present ; the density of cations in the neighbourhood of the surface is therefore increased. The ionic atmosphere becomes, so to speak, compressed near the surface. This fact is expressed by the broken line in the diagram.

Every electrolyte thus decreases ζ even although ϵ is unaltered. This is just what we have found in the preceding paragraphs. If, however, the added ion is divalent, the electrostatic attraction is much stronger than if it were univalent, and if it were trivalent the attraction would be stronger still. Correspondingly, the " compression " of the ionic atmosphere is more marked in these cases. Here we have the reason for the effect of the valency of the ion oppositely charged to the ions adsorbed on the surface. If the ion, moreover, is strongly adsorbed (as, for example, the fuchsine ion, see p. 106) then the charge on the surface may be decreased by adsorption of the ion, and this effect thus augments the effect of the ion on the atmosphere. Such ions have therefore an effect greater than would be expected from their charge alone.

We must now enquire which ions may in fact modify ϵ, the total potential difference between wall and liquid. A similar potential difference is established between a metal placed in a solution of its ions, and in this case the potential is well known to be determined by the standard electrode potential of the metal, and the concentration of the ions in the solution :

$$E = E^0 + [RT/nF] \log c.$$

For the metal the common ions are thus *potential determining* ions.

A similar statement is also true for non-metals. Consider a salt, say, silver iodide, in contact with its saturated solution. In this particular case, measurements both of ϵ and of ζ show the silver iodide to be negatively charged with respect to the solution, so that the silver ions may be assumed to have passed into solution to a greater extent than the iodide ions. If, now, potassium iodide is added to the solution, the common ion effect causes the silver ion concentration to decrease, so that the negative potential difference should become greater, as in fact it does. On the other hand, the addition of silver nitrate will increase the silver ion concentration, so that the potential difference becomes smaller, then zero, and at greater concentrations positive.

For a ferric hydroxide surface similar reasoning indicates that ferric ions and hydroxyl ions will affect the potential. Thus it may be stated generally that the common ions of the surface material are potential determining ions.

Potential determining ions can thus increase ϵ and also ζ, but all other ions will compress the atmosphere of opposite ions and will thus lower ζ without altering ϵ.*

We may now refer back to the glass electrode which was described on p. 77. It is easy to see that with it we measure the ϵ potential between glass and water, while by determining streaming potentials in a glass capillary we obtain ζ. It now becomes quite clear that, as stated on p. 77, the ϵ potential of the glass electrode is exclusively determined by the potential-determining hydrogen ions and is independent of other ions, but the streaming potential which is connected with the ζ potential, is affected by the addition of any cation because an indifferent ion leaves ϵ unchanged but compresses the opposing ionic atmosphere.

* For the sake of completeness it should be stated that circumstances can arise when indifferent electrolytes do effect ϵ. We shall not, however, go into this matter further.

CHAPTER VI

COLLOIDS

1. Colloids

THE characteristic properties of so-called colloidal substances were first recognized during the nineteenth century. The Italian, Francesco Selmi, showed that, under certain conditions, it was possible to obtain what appeared to be solutions of substances which were usually only very slightly soluble, such as silver chloride, sulphur, and Prussian blue. These solutions resembled in many respects those of glue, starch, or albumin. The British scientist, Thomas Graham, pointed out that glue, starch, and similar substances were not crystalline in the solid state, and that silver chloride and the other substances mentioned above could be precipitated in apparently shapeless, amorphous masses. He called those substances which crystallize readily, such as sugar, common salt, etc., *crystalloids*, and the other substances *colloids*. Solutions of crystalloids were " true solutions " ; those of colloids were " colloidal solutions." Later work has shown that the distinction between crystalloids and colloids cannot be maintained in its original sense. It will be seen from what follows that the characteristics of colloidal solutions are not simply bound up with the crystalline or non-crystalline nature of the substance in the solid state.

Graham made a further very important observation which really strikes to the root of the matter. He noticed that the substances present in colloidal solutions diffused very slowly.

It can be shown that for approximately spherical particles in a solution the diffusion constant (see Chapter I) is inversely proportional to the radius. Thus, as the particles present in a colloidal solution diffuse more slowly than those in a true solution they must be larger. There are two possibilities : either (a) we are concerned with large molecules, or (b) we are concerned with large aggregates of small molecules.

Yet, originally, there was some difficulty in regarding colloidal solutions simply as solutions containing very large particles. For example, they cannot be separated from the solvent by filtration, at any rate with filter paper. Graham did, however, show that colloidal solutions would not pass through parchment paper, although solutes in true solution would do so. This process, known as dialysis, makes it possible to separate colloids from a solution containing both colloids and substances in true solution ; the substances in true solution will pass through a parchment paper, and can thus be removed. Fig. 45 shows such a dialyser. Nowadays the parchment paper membrane is replaced by a collodion membrane, or even more recently by cellophane.

A second difficulty was the fact that no colloidal solution when viewed under the microscope, even with the greatest magnification, revealed the presence of any such large particles. We shall see in the next section how this difficulty was overcome.

In addition to proteins, polysaccharides, etc.—the so-called natural colloids, or bio-colloids —there are many other substances, such as the above-mentioned silver chloride, sulphur, and Prussian blue, which can be obtained in solutions in which they show slow diffusion, and which must,

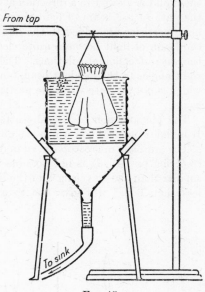

FIG. 45.

therefore, contain comparatively large particles. If, for example, hydrogen sulphide is passed into a solution of arsenious oxide, no arsenious sulphide is precipitated, but an orange-yellow solution is obtained, which, in agreement with what has been said above, shows no elevation of the boiling point, lowering of the freezing point, or osmotic pressure. The " dissolved " substance cannot pass through parchment paper, and yet the solution appears perfectly clear under the microscope. If dilute solutions of silver nitrate and potassium iodide are mixed, under certain conditions (see p. 135) silver iodide is not precipitated, but remains in colloidal solution. If a solution of chlorauric acid, $HAuCl_4$, is reduced, certain precautions being taken, the following reaction takes place :

$$HAuCl_4 + 3H \rightarrow Au + 4HCl.$$

The gold formed is not precipitated, but remains in a clear solution, sometimes coloured red, sometimes blue.

2 Ultramicroscopy

There is, however, a method that removes any doubt as to whether or not these colloidal solutions contain the dissolved substance in the form of larger particles than are present in true solutions. If a beam of light is passed through pure water or through a salt solution, and the liquid is viewed in a direction at right angles to the incident beam, the path of the beam of light through the liquid cannot be seen. If, now, particles are added to the liquid to make it turbid, the path of the beam of light becomes quite clear. This is just what happens in the case of colloidal solutions. There is a scattering of the light at right angles to the incident beam, and this scattered light is polarized, which is not the case when the particles giving rise to the turbidity are coarse.

The phenomenon of lateral scattering is called the Tyndall effect. It is the principle upon which the ultramicroscope rests.

The ordinary microscope, even in its most perfect form, has a limited resolving power. It is not possible to see with it particles which are smaller than the wavelength of the light used. A particle of diameter less than $0 \cdot 1\mu$* will give rise to a diffraction effect, but it is not

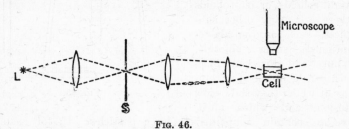

FIG. 46.

possible to distinguish it from the incident light. In the ordinary microscope one looks into the incident light ; a local, very small decrease in the intensity of the light cannot be detected, just as in daylight the stars cannot be seen in the heavens as a small increase in the intensity of the light. Ultramicroscopy therefore depends on a method of illumination shown diagrammatically in Fig. 46. If the solution is observed with the microscope in a direction perpendicular to the light from the source, nothing is seen unless a particle happens to be in the path of the light, and gives rise to a diffraction pattern. This diffraction pattern will be seen in the microscope against a dark background. The ultramicroscope, where the light scattered laterally from the individual particles is viewed, thus gives a more detailed view of the Tyndall effect. It is thus clear that in the ultramicroscope particles considerably smaller than the wavelength of the light used can be " seen," although it is not the particles themselves that are viewed but the diffraction patterns to which they give rise. It must be remembered that the form, colour, and size of the diffraction pattern is no direct measure of the form, colour, and size of the object, so that the results of ultramicroscopy are still somewhat limited. It is, however,

* 1μ (micron) $= 10^{-3}$ mm. $1m\mu$ (millimicron) $= 10^{-3}\mu = 10^{-6}$ mm.

possible to make certain deductions about the shape of the colloidal particles from the type of image obtained in the ultramicroscope.

If a colloidal solution, for example a gold sol (colloidal solutions are usually called sols, an abbreviation of solution), is investigated with the ultramicroscope, bright discs are seen on a completely black background. Not all colloidal solutions give such a beautiful image ; in general it is only the so-called hydrophobic colloids such as gold sol, arsenious sulphide sol, etc., which give good and readily distinguishable diffraction discs. So-called hydrophilic colloids such as protein solutions often give rise to undifferentiated patterns, i.e. to a patch of light and no more. We shall deal with the difference between these two groups later (see p. 124).

The ultramicroscope shows with certainty that a number of typical colloidal solutions contain very fine particles in suspension which cannot be distinguished by the ordinary microscope.

3. Determination of Particle Size

It was naturally a matter of some importance to determine the size of the colloidal particles thus made visible. As has been stated above this is not possible by direct measurement of the diffraction pattern obtained. Zsigmondy devised a method which can be used in many cases.

Suppose we have a gold sol of which the gold content is known. The gold sol is brought under the ultramicroscope, and by means of a diaphragm in the eye-piece part of the field of view is delimited. The dimensions of the field of view are measured by means of an ocular micrometer or graticule. The depth of the field of view can be measured with the aid of the slit S in Fig. 46, which can be turned through 90° by a lever. What was the depth of the illuminated part is now the breadth, and can be measured with the ocular micrometer. The number of particles which are present in the volume, now known, is counted. Since the particles are, of course, moving about with the Brownian movement (see p. 5), the number which are in the field of view from instant to instant is different. This difficulty is overcome by taking the mean of, say, a hundred counts. Next the number of particles present in 1 c.c. is calculated. Since the concentration of the solution and the specific gravity of gold are known, the mean size of one of the particles can be calculated. Zsigmondy found that the particles in a gold sol were visible in the ultramicroscope if they had a diameter greater than 6 mμ. In general particles down to 0·2 μ diameter (*i.e.* 200 mμ) are visible in the ordinary microscope. These are called *microns*. Particles of diameter between 200 mμ and 6 mμ are visible in the ultramicroscope and are called *ultramicrons*. Particles which are too small to be visible in the ultramicroscope are called *amicrons*.

We have seen on p. 6 that the size of suspended particles can be determined from the rate of sedimentation by means of Stokes' law, but in that case we were dealing with gamboge particles with diameters of the order of $0.5\ \mu$. Colloidal particles are much smaller, and it would be necessary to wait for years before there was any visible settling. The centrifuge, however, provides a field of force similar to the gravitational field but many times stronger. The speed with which the suspended particles are rotated is measured. The equation given on p. 6 still holds, except that the acceleration due to gravity, g, in the lower equation on p. 6 is replaced by the centrifugal force. Svedberg, in particular, has constructed ultracentrifuges capable of rotating with 85,000 revolutions per minute, and in which the centrifugal force is 250,000 times stronger than gravity. By determinations with this instrument the size of particles in colloidal solutions can be calculated. This method is of particular importance in the case of biocolloids, which give no distinguishable patterns in the ultramicroscope.

Other possible methods of determining the size of colloidal particles will be dealt with on pp. 150 and 151.

4. Electron-microscopy

The ultramicroscope and the ultracentrifuge thus give us information about particle size, but only to a very limited degree do they enable us to state the form of the particles. The introduction of the electron-microscope was a great step forward in this respect. The resolving power of the ordinary optical microscope is limited by the wavelength of light to, say, some tenths of a micron. When it was discovered that the electron had a wave nature and that the wavelength was a fraction of an Angstrom unit (10^{-8}cm.) it became possible to achieve a much greater resolving power by using beams of electrons instead of beams of light. Electrons are refracted in electric and magnetic fields, and by suitable arrangements such fields can be used as lenses for beams of electrons, bringing them to a focus at a certain point. Considerable magnification can thus be effected (up to 100,000 diameters). For visual examination the electron image is focused on to a fluorescent screen (a screen covered with zinc sulphide, for example). It is also possible to replace the fluorescent screen with a photographic plate.

The electron-microscope has increased our knowledge of the form of small particles considerably, and it has been largely used in biology to reveal details of such things as viruses, cell nuclei, the structure of bacteria, etc., which could not be seen with the optical microscope.

A difficulty associated with the electron-microscope is the fact that the whole process must be carried out in a high vacuum. Thus,

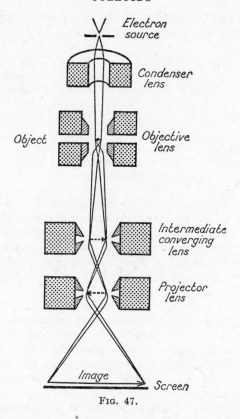

Fig. 47.

solutions cannot be examined, and biological specimens must be rigorously " outgassed " before they can be submitted to examination.

5. Degree of Dispersion

We have seen in Chapter I that it is possible to determine the size of molecules. It is known, for example, that a hydrogen molecule has a diameter of about $0\cdot 1$ mμ, and a benzene molecule a diameter of about $0\cdot 3$ mμ. It is seen from these figures that molecules belong to the class of amicrons.

We thus come to the conclusion that substances suspended in a solvent can be classified according to their degree of fineness, or to use a word commonly employed in colloid science and introduced by Ostwald, substances can be dispersed in various degrees in the solvent. When the suspended substance is very finely divided it is said to have a high degree of dispersion ; coarser particles are said to have a low degree of dispersion. The scheme on p. 122 gives a rough classification, and shows how certain properties of disperse systems gradually change with the degree of dispersion.

1μ	500 mμ	100mμ	10 mμ	1 mμ	$0\cdot1$ mμ
microns		ultramicrons		amicrons	
suspensions		colloids		molecularly disperse systems	
are held back by filter paper		do not pass a dialysis membrane		do pass a dialysis membrane, but not a semi-permeable membrane	
sediment rapidly		sediment slowly		stable	
can be centrifuged		can be separated by ultra-centrifuge		stable	

It is seen from this table that the properties which we have recognized as belonging to colloidal systems agree approximately with those of systems in which the degree of disperson falls between 1 μ and 1 mμ.

In general, then, suspensions with particles greater than 1 μ in diameter may be classed as gross mechanical suspensions ; colloidal systems have a degree of dispersion between 1 μ and 1 mμ, and true solutions between 1 mμ and $0\cdot1$ mμ.

Thus, there is a continuous gradation of size from true solutions, through colloidal solutions, to mechanical suspensions.

In colloidal systems it is usual to distinguish between the dispersion medium (the liquid) and the disperse phase (the particles). The terms external and internal phase are sometimes used ; also, the particles of the disperse phase are sometimes referred to as micelles, and the dispersion medium as the intermicellar liquid.

A colloidal solution in which the disperse phase is water is called a hydrosol ; if the disperse phase is alcohol or benzene the terms are alcosol or benzosol, respectively.

Whether a solution is colloidal or not is a matter of degree of dispersion. It is necessary to distinguish between substances with small molecules and those with very large ones. As far as those with small molecules are concerned there are two possibilities :

1. The substance is very soluble (for example, sugar in water) ; in other words the substance has a great tendency to become molecularly disperse up to high concentrations in the solvent.

2. The substance is sparingly soluble (for example, silver iodide in water). The substance has hardly any tendency to become molecularly disperse in water, but it is possible for it to become dispersed as " poly-molecular " particles in the solvent (strictly, in the saturated solution). In most cases such substances exist in the solid state as ionic or atomic crystals, and it is small portions of these crystals which constitute the micelles.

As far as substances with large molecules are concerned there are those which have such large molecules that even if they have a tendency to become molecularly disperse, a colloidal solution results, simply because the single molecules themselves have dimensions which necessarily bring the solution into the middle column of the above scheme. Examples of this are provided by many biocolloids and the products of polymerization of organic substances (such as polystyrene). These so-called macromolecules, which are at once molecularly disperse and colloidal, have recently attained great importance. We shall study them further at a later stage (Chapter IX).

Fig. 48 gives a schematic representation of the sizes of some particles in order to give the student a better picture of the proportional sizes of microns, ultramicrons, and amicrons.

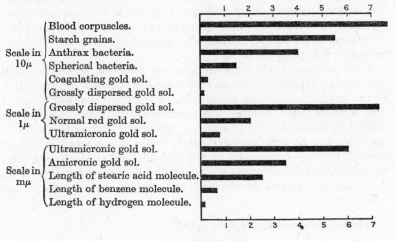

Scale in 10μ
- Blood corpuscles.
- Starch grains.
- Anthrax bacteria.
- Spherical bacteria.
- Coagulating gold sol.
- Grossly dispersed gold sol.

Scale in 1μ
- Grossly dispersed gold sol.
- Normal red gold sol.
- Ultramicronic gold sol.

Scale in mμ
- Ultramicronic gold sol.
- Amicronic gold sol.
- Length of stearic acid molecule.
- Length of benzene molecule.
- Length of hydrogen molecule.

FIG. 48.

From the foregoing it should be obvious why colloidal solutions have very small osmotic pressures, elevations of the boiling point, and depressions of the freezing point. We have seen in Chapter I (see p. 17) that these phenomena are determined by the number of particles present per litre. As we have now shown that the particles in a colloidal solution are relatively large, it follows that their number must be correspondingly small for a solution of a given concentration. The following calculations will make this point clear.

Consider a gold sol with a concentration of 0·1 per cent. with particles 4 mμ in diameter. Working in round numbers we may say that since 1 litre of solution contains 1 gm. of gold, the volume of the gold particles will be 50 cu. mm. (the specific gravity of gold is 19). The volume of a particle is $4 \times 4 \times 4$ mμ^3 or, say, 50 mμ^3. 1 litre of solution thus contains 10^{18} gold particles. Now, the osmotic pressure of a solution which contains 1 gm.-mol. (6×10^{22} independent particles) in 22·4 litres is 1 atmosphere at 0° C. We thus see that the gold sol will have an osmotic pressure of 0·5 mm. of water, and a freezing point depression of 0·000004°. The calculation of the number of independent particles thus leads immediately to the conclusion that osmotic pressure phenomena, as well as boiling point elevation or freezing point lowering, are negligibly small.

Osmotic pressures can only be measured accurately if they amount to at least a few mm. of water. The lowering of the freezing point must be at least 0·001° to be measurable. The values for the gold sol are thus both less than these limiting values. At the same time, it will be seen that if the colloidal solution contained more independent particles, the osmotic pressure might perhaps come within range of possibility of measurement, but that the freezing point lowering (and boiling point elevation) would still lie outside the range of observation. We shall return to this point on p. 151.

It is, perhaps, worth while to point out that the determination of the osmotic pressure (as far as that is possible) gives a determination of the number of particles per litre (see p. 123) and thus of the size of the particles ; but whether this number can be called a molecular weight is doubtful. We saw on pp. 122 and 123 that the colloidal particles can be polymolecular (silver iodide has a small molecular weight, but is polymolecular in colloidal solution) or single molecules of macromolecular substances. In the first case the (chemical) molecular weight does not coincide with the particle weight, in the second case it does.

6. Hydrophobic and Hydrophilic Colloids

Colloidal solutions may be classified into two main types ; it should, however, be clearly understood that this classification is even less absolute than, say, that between inorganic and organic chemistry. However, be that as it may, the two groups show such divergent behaviour that it is necessary to make the distinction if we are to study the properties of colloidal solutions systematically.

If, for the time being, we consider only water as the dispersion medium, one group contains colloidal solutions such as those of metals, hydroxides, and salts, while the other is composed chiefly of proteins and the higher carbohydrates.

The first group are called hydrophobic, and the second hydrophilic colloids, for a reason which will appear shortly.

The members of the first group are very sensitive to the addition of electrolytes. Very small quantities are sufficient to cause the colloidal solution to coagulate, i.e. to cause the disperse phase to separate in flocks. In the ultramicroscope hydrophobic colloids give a well-differentiated pattern, and finally, their physical properties differ very little from those of the pure dispersion medium. A gold sol and an arsenious sulphide sol, for example, have practically the same viscosity as pure water.

In the case of the second group, all these properties are just reversed. Large quantities of electrolytes are necessary to cause them to separate from the dispersion medium. In the ultramicroscope they give only a diffuse spot of light. The viscosity is very different from that of water.

A very typical difference can also be seen in the methods of preparation of colloidal solutions. Substances of the second group form colloidal solutions when the dry solid is merely shaken with water. For substances of the first group this is not possible. Sols such as gold sol, silver iodide sol, and arsenious sulphide sol can only be obtained by indirect methods (p. 117).

The great differences between these groups has led to the adoption of special names for them. Formerly the terms *suspensoid* and *emulsoid* were largely used, but they give the impression that in colloidal solutions of the first type the disperse phase is a solid, whereas in the other it is a liquid. This classification is incorrect ; if it were correct it would not have been necessary to explain how the above-named differences vary with the state of aggregation of the disperse phase. There is the distinction between *organic* and *inorganic* colloids, since inorganic substances often give a sol of a hydrophobic nature, whereas most hydrophilic colloids consist of organic substances. But these differences do not go to the root of the question. The terms *reversible* and *irreversible* colloids are based upon more essential differences. They refer to the fact that if the disperse phase is precipitated by electrolytes or by evaporation of the solvent it will, or will not, return to the colloidal state again by simple dilution with the solvent. These names derive from the difference in visible behaviour of the colloids. The explanation of this difference is not a matter concerned with the disperse phase alone, but is to be considered in relation to the environment of the disperse substance—i.e. in relation to the medium. The colloidal particles may just be dispersed, or the dispersed particles may have some special interaction with the dispersion medium. One therefore refers (very reasonably) to hydrophobic and hydrophilic colloids, or more generally, since these terms refer to water as the dispersion medium, to lyophobic and lyophilic colloids. These names indicate that the colloidal particles have a hatred of (Greek, *phobein* = fleeing from, dread of), or a liking for (Greek *philein* = love) the dispersion medium (Greek, *hudor* = water, *los* = dissolve).

CHAPTER VII

HYDROPHOBIC COLLOIDS

1. Crystalline Nature of Hydrophobic Particles

In 1912 von Laue discovered that when X-rays are passed through a crystalline plate they give rise to characteristic diffraction patterns. This observation made it possible to discover whether a substance was crystalline or not. Debye and Scherrer, in 1917, developed a method whereby these interference phenomena could be produced if the substance were not in the form of a crystalline plate, but in the form of a crystalline powder, in which, from the nature of the case, the different crystallites would lie in arbitrary positions. Very definite interference patterns are obtained in the form of circles, from the relative positions of which it is possible to draw conclusions concerning the crystalline form of the substance.

Scherrer applied this method of investigation to colloidal systems, and came to the important conclusion that the particles in colloidal solutions, at any rate in the case of nearly all hydrophobic colloids, are crystalline. Thus there is no antithesis between the crystalline and colloidal states ; on the contrary the disperse phase in many colloidal solutions is crystalline. Although the particles when precipitated, appear to be in the amorphous state, X-ray investigation shows that the precipitate is not amorphous but microcrystalline.

2. Stability of Hydrophobic Sols

The possibility of the existence of hydrophobic colloids cannot be ascribed to the tendency of the dispersed particles to spread themselves spontaneously through the solvent ; this would require a high degree of hydrophilic nature. In the case of hydrophobic colloids we are concerned, to all intents and purposes, with insoluble substances which, for a reason to be investigated below, have distributed themselves throughout the solvent (or more correctly, the saturated solution) as polymolecular aggregates. The question which immediately arises is why the small particles do not unite to form larger aggregates We have seen above (p. 92) that at the boundary of a phase there is always a surface tension. It is, therefore, at first sight difficult to understand why this surface energy does not yield to the tendency to make the surface as small as possible ; that is to say, why it does not attempt to make the particles combine. We must remember, too, that these particles are in constant Brownian motion, and that all the conditions are satisfactory for the particles to be brought together and to remain together. The problem before us, then, is how these colloidal systems are maintained as such, and how it is possible for a colloidal solution of gold to be stable for many years without any visible change taking place.

The answer to this question is to be found in the fact that the colloidal particles are all electrically charged. They are surrounded by an electrical double layer, and this prevents them from approaching each other too closely. They repel each other, so that material collisions do not take place and hence coagulation cannot occur. In an ultra-microscope the particles do indeed appear to collide. It must, however, be remembered that it is not the particles themselves that are seen in the ultramicroscope, but the much larger diffraction patterns to which they give rise (p. 118).

The fact that the colloidal particles do carry an electrical double layer can be arrived at immediately from the observation that they show electrophoretic transport, which we discussed in a previous chapter.

In the year 1900, Hardy showed that if a certain sol with which he was experimenting contained caustic potash the particles were negatively charged, but if the sol contained acid the particles were positively charged. These facts were discovered from the direction of the electrophoretic transport. If the sol were just neutralized, there was no electrophoretic transport and the sol coagulated. Hardy thus arrived at the conclusion that a sol is only stable when it carries an electric charge. At what he called the *isoelectric point* the sol became unstable and coagulated. Hardy's views have received ample confirmation. For instance, Burton added small quantities of an aluminium salt to a gold sol. The concentrations of the added aluminium are given in the first column of the table below. In the second column is the electrophoretic velocity of the particles,* and in the third column the properties of the sol.

mg. Al per litre	Electrophoretic velocity in μ per sec. per volt/cm.	Properties of the sol
0	3·30 (towards the anode)	Indefinitely stable.
0·19	1·71 (towards the anode)	Coagulates after 4 hrs.
	0	Coagulates immediately.
0·38	0·17 (towards the cathode)	Coagulates after 4 hrs.
0·65	1·35 (towards the cathode)	Not completely coagulated after 4 days.

* On pp. 58–59, we saw that the velocity per volt per cm. of most ions lay between 30 and 70 × 10⁻⁵ cm. per sec. (i.e. between 3 and 7μ per second). Ions and colloidal particles thus move at approximately the same speed in the electric field.

It is clear from this table that Hardy's view is confirmed, and at the same time the statement that the stability of a hydrophobic colloid depends closely on its electrical properties as determined by electro-kinetic measurements (ζ potential, see p. 107) is verified.

The behaviour of these colloidal solutions thus clearly depends on two opposing factors : an attractive force (A) which tends to bring the particles together, and a repulsive force (R) which tends to keep

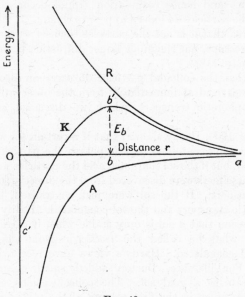

FIG. 49.

them apart. The curves in Fig. 49 represent the state of affairs. The abscissæ represent the distances between two particles, and the ordinates the potential energy which the particles possess at each distance. The curve A is the curve of attraction which we have already come across in Fig. 30 (the student should again read what is said about it on p. 92) ; the curve R is the curve of electrical repulsion. The attractive force varies inversely as r^7, and hence the potential energy of attraction varies inversely as r^6 (curve A). Similarly, the repulsive force varies inversely as r^2 (Coulomb's law) and so the repulsive potential varies inversely as r (curve R). Curve A is therefore much steeper than curve R. It is evident that the repulsion does not reach beyond the electrical double layer. We have seen on p. 114 that electrolytes, particularly those with bi- or polyvalent counter ions, compress the double layer. Consequently they decrease the range of the repulsion. Potential-determining ions, which are capable of increasing or decreasing the surface potential, make the repulsion more or less strong. Curve K is the resultant of curves A and R, and thus represents the total mutual potential energy of the two particles as a function of the distance between them. Since the state where the particles have the smallest potential energy is the state of equilibrium (a stone released from a height falls to the earth where it has a minimum potential energy), the point c' represents the equilibrium state ; that is, there is equilibrium when the distance apart of the particles is zero, or in other words when the particles coalesce. But let us see how this coalescence comes about. The particles are, shall we say, initially at a distance a apart, and as they approach each other the distance b must be passed. From a to b the potential energy does not decrease ; it does, in fact, increase. It is true that after the point b is reached there is a rapid decrease in potential energy as the distance becomes smaller, but to go from a to b will be difficult because the potential energy increases to a maximum value of E_b.

It is clear, then, that an energy " hill " has to be surmounted. A similar state of affairs has been referred to on p. 37.

In addition to potential energy the particle also possess kinetic energy. The kinetic energy, $\frac{1}{2}mv^2$, of the Brownian motion (see pp. 5, 7) might be sufficient to overcome the energy hill. The stability of the sol thus depends on which is the greater, E_b or $\frac{1}{2}mv^2$. On p. 7 it was shown that the kinetic energy is equal to $\frac{3RT}{2N}$; on p. 2 we replaced $\frac{R}{N}$ by k. The sol will therefore be stable if ^3kT is less than E_b.

As has been mentioned above the position of the repulsion curve R depends on the electrolyte content of the solution. As the attraction curve is very steep, the most important aspect of the repulsion curve is its range. If there are repulsive forces over large enough distances, the resultant will show a maximum ; but if the forces are only small at small distances, the maximum will be very low or non-existent. This explains why hydrophobic colloids lose their stability by addition of electrolytes that always decrease the range of the repulsion, hence lowering the maximum in curve K or causing it to vanish, and at the same time lowering the ζ potential. The greater the ζ potential of the double layer the more stable is the sol. Conversely, there is a lower limit, the so-called critical potential, at which E_b becomes equal to, or less than, $\frac{3}{2}kT$, and the sol becomes unstable.

Of course, individual particles may have a greater velocity than the mean value, so that the approach of two particles will occasionally result in their coalescence, even at temperatures where $3kT/2$ is less than E_b. However, the number of particles with sufficient velocity and kinetic energy for this to happen, decreases rapidly as the ζ potential and hence E_b increases.

3. The Coagulating Effect of Electrolytes

We may summarize the results of the above discussion by saying that colloidal particles remain in this state because of their electrical properties. Electrolytes have a coagulating effect which is dependent upon the extent to which they lower the ζ potential, that is, upon the extent to which they compress the double layer. The flocculating action of electrolytes therefore depends on their effect on the double layer, which has already been discussed extensively on p. 112 ff. The rules mentioned there will therefore be those which also govern coagulation.

As far back as the end of the last century Schulze, and a little later Linder and Picton, put forward the following rule for the coagulation of colloids by inorganic salts : the coagulating effect of a salt is determined by the valency of the ion which carries a charge opposite to that of the particles concerned. The cation of the electrolyte thus governs the coagulation of a negatively charged sol, whilst the anion is concerned in the precipitation of a positively charged sol. It is clear that this result is exactly the same as that which we have encountered in the case of the electrokinetic processes on p. 106 ; and this analogy goes even further. Organic ions, the hydrogen ion, the hydroxyl ion, and the ions of the heavy metals have a greater coagulating effect than would be expected from their valency. There is obviously a close connection between the process of coagulation and the electrokinetic effect dealt with previously.

The following table, which gives the limiting values in millimols per litre for the concentration of electrolytes which coagulate an arsenious sulphide sol, will make this point clearer. By the limiting value is understood the concentration of electrolyte which is just capable of precipitating the colloid completely in a given time (in this case, two hours).

Univalent cations		Divalent cations		Trivalent cations	
LiCl	58	$MgCl_2$	0·72	$AlCl_3$	0·093
NaCl	51	$MgSO_4$	0·81	$Al(NO_3)_3$	0·095
KCl	50	$CaCl_2$	0·65	$\frac{1}{2}Al_2(SO_4)_3$	0·096
KNO_3	50	$SrCl_2$	0·63	$Ce(NO_3)_3$	0·080
HCl	31	$BaCl_2$	0·69		
$\frac{1}{2}H_2SO_4$	30	$ZnCl_2$	0·69		
Aniline hydrochloride	2·5	$UO_2(NO_3)_2$	0·64		
Morphine hydrochloride	0·42	*Quinine sulphate*	0·24		
New fuchsine	0·11	*Benzidine nitrate*	0·087		

This table brings out clearly the great difference in the coagulating powers of ions of different valency. If we confine our attention to the usual inorganic ions (in ordinary type) we see that the univalent ions, such as the potassium ion, K^+, have a limiting value of about 50 millimols, the divalent ions, such as the barium ion, Ba^{++}, have a limiting value of about 0·68 millimols, and the trivalent ions, such as the aluminium ion, Al^{+++}, one of less than 0·1 millimols per litre.

We can therefore say that the coagulating powers of the ions K^+, Ba^{++}, and Al^{+++} are in the ratio of $\dfrac{1}{50} : \dfrac{1}{0·68} : \dfrac{1}{0·09}$ or as $1 : 75 : 580$.

This ratio is nearly equal to $1 : 2^6 : 3^6$.

A corresponding table could be given for a positively charged sol, from which a similar proportionality would be seen to hold for uni-, di-, and trivalent anions, for example, Cl^-, SO_4^{--}, and PO_4^{---}, whilst the organic ions and the hydroxyl ion occupy special positions.

The explanation of this valency effect, known as the rule of Schulze and Hardy, can be derived directly from what has been said already on p. 129 about the influence of electrolytes on the maximum of the potential energy curve. From the experiments of Hardy and Burton the close connection between colloidal stability and the ζ potential has been made clear. On p. 114 it was seen that added electrolytes increase the density of the opposing ionic atmosphere, thus making the potential curve steeper. If the added ions are polyvalent the process is more effective and is no longer simply proportional to the valency but to a much higher power (the valency appears as an exponent, and not as a coefficient). The effect is, of course, augmented if the coagulating ion is strongly adsorbed on the surface of the colloidal particles.

That the ions which have a charge of the same sign as that of the colloid (anions, for example, with respect to a negatively charged sol) have little effect, is also readily understood. The particles attract oppositely charged ions, but repel ions with a similar charge, so that these latter ions can exert no great influence on the coagulation process. They are not quite without influence, however. From the accompanying table it is seen that anions do play some little part in bringing about

Electrolyte	Limiting value	Nature of the Anion
Potassium citrate^{---}	>240	Organic, strongly adsorbed, polyvalent.
acetate$^-$	110	Organic, strongly adsorbed
formate$^-$	86	Organic, strongly adsorbed
sulphate^{--}	66	inorganic, polyvalent
chloride$^-$	50	normal
nitrate$^-$	50	normal

the coagulation of a negatively charged arsenious sulphide sol, As_2S_3, and that their effect is in general determined by their charge and their adsorbability.

4. Some Special Cases of Coagulation

(a) *Mutual coagulation.* If two sols composed of particles with charges of opposite sign are brought together, electrical repulsion is replaced by attraction. The admixture of the negatively charged arsenious oxide and the positively charged ferric oxide sol is represented by Fig. 50. The ordinates represent the extent of coagulation, the abscissæ the ratio of the quantities of the sols mixed. The shaded portion gives the area where coagulation takes place, and the unshaded

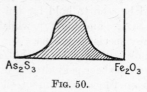

As_2S_3 Fe_2O_3

FIG. 50.

part indicates where the sol is not coagulated. If a little ferric oxide sol is added to a large quantity of an arsenious sulphide sol, the few positively charged particles attach themselves to the excess of negatively charged particles ; the surface potential of these particles will fall, but the excess potential exerts a sufficient repelling force on the particles of sol remaining. In proportion as the quantity of positively charged sol increases, the maximum of Fig. 49 falls and before long coagulation takes place. A similar state of affairs holds for an excess of a ferric oxide sol to which a little arsenious sulphide sol is added. Fig. 50 with its maximum of mutual coagulation is thus explained.

(b) *Irregular series.* If a negatively charged arsenious sulphide sol is coagulated by the addition of aluminium chloride in varying concentrations, the following sequence of events is seen to take place. For very small concentrations there is no coagulation ; as the limiting value is

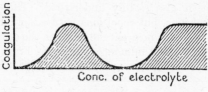

Conc. of electrolyte

FIG. 51.

reached there is coagulation ; for somewhat higher concentrations there is again no coagulation, and at higher concentrations still coagulation again occurs. It may thus be said that for increasing concentration of the added electrolyte there is an initial non-coagulation zone, then a first coagulation zone, then a second non-coagulation zone, and finally a second coagulation zone. Fig. 51 shows this diagrammatically by a method exactly analogous to Fig. 50. If the student glances at

Fig. 43, p. 112 this behaviour will immediately become clear. It is there pointed out that aluminium hydroxide, the hydrolysis product of aluminium chloride, is a positively charged colloid. This brings about a mutual coagulation of the arsenious sulphide sol (first coagulation zone). If more aluminium salt is added the aluminium ions are adsorbed at the surface of the arsenious sulphide particles and eventually produce a positive ζ potential great enough for E_b to exceed $\frac{3}{2}kT$. In the second coagulation zone we therefore have a positively charged sol. If still more aluminium chloride is added, the chloride ions eventually compress the double layer so much that the ζ potential, and hence the repulsion maximum, falls below the critical value. This phenomenon is called (not very happily) an irregular series.

We saw on p. 65 that hydrolysis is a phenomenon depending on the pH of the medium ; this also holds for the irregular series, which, as described above, is caused by hydrolysis.

The phenomenon of the irrregular series can, of course, also be due to another cause. A strongly adsorbed cation, such, for example, as strychnine hydrochloride, causes a reversal of sign, which is also shown in Fig. 43. Such an electrolyte thus brings about coagulation in the manner shown in Fig. 51.

5. The Stannic Oxide Sol

In the years 1913 and 1914 Zsigmondy and his co-workers carried out some investigations on stannic oxide, SnO_2, sol. Such a sol is prepared from precipitated stannic oxide, which, after prolonged washing, is brought into colloidal solution by means of acid or alkali. If acid is used, the sol is positively charged ; if alkali, negatively.

Limiting Values for SnO_2 *Sol in Milli-equivalents per 10 c.c.*

Sol $\frac{SnO_2}{KOH}$	2	10	25	50	100
NaCl	1·8	1·7	0·34	0·26	0·14
NaNO$_3$ . . .	1·9	1·5	0·30	0·28	0·14
Na$_2$SO$_4$ . . .	1·8	1·7	0·32	0·28	0·14
NaH$_2$ citrate . .	2·3	2·0	0·40	0·52	0·50
HCl	0·33	0·07	0·025	0·0135	0·007
CaCl$_2$	0·33	0·075	0·022	0·0135	0·007
BaCl$_2$	0·35	0·065	0·022	0·0130	0·007
AlCl$_3$	0·33	0·07	0·025	0·0135	0·007
Al(NO$_3$)$_3$ . . .	0·33	0·075	0·025	0·0140	0·007
AgNO$_3$. . . .	—	—	0·025	0·0180	0·009
Alkali in 10 c.c. sol .	0·333	0·065	0·026	0·013	0·0064

These investigations led to the following results. If the limiting values for stannic oxide sols prepared by the action of caustic potash are determined, the results given in the table on p. 133 are obtained. The top line gives the ratio of the quantity of oxide to alkali used in the preparation of the sol. The sols referred to in columns 2 to 6 thus differ in the ratio of dispersed substance to added alkali. It is seen from the table that for each of the sols the limiting value for the univalent alkali metal ions is practically the same, whilst that for all remaining ions, no matter what their valency, is lower, although the values are almost the same between themselves. Here, then, we have a behaviour which is considerably different from that of the arsenious sulphide sol, the silver iodide sol, the gold sol, and many other hydrophobic sols. What can be the reason for this difference ?

The key to the explanation lies in the bottom line of the table. If we calculate the concentration of potassium hydroxide in each of the sols we find just the same value as the limiting value of the electrolytes given in the second part of the table. If we remember that the stannates (derived from H_2SnO_3) of the cations in this part of the table are all insoluble (H_2SnO_3 itself excluded) the following explanation comes to mind. The stannic oxide particles prepared with a little alkali owe their charge to a double layer which has not hydroxyl ions, but stannate ions (SnO_3^{--}) in the inner layer. The added potassium hydroxide reacts chemically with the molecules which are situated in the outer layer of the stannic oxide particle. The potassium stannate, K_2SnO_3, thus formed gives rise to the double layer, the anions forming the inner

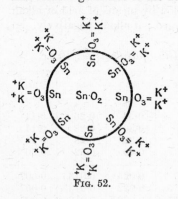

layer and the potassium ions, K^+, the outer (see Fig. 52). If now an electrolyte is added which can form an insoluble stannate in the double layer, the double layer disappears, and with it the potential difference, because there is now no soluble electrolyte present which could give rise to this double layer.

We therefore meet here a mechanism of coagulation which differs from that which we have encountered up to the present. Nevertheless our former explanation covers this case too—that

Fig. 52.

the reduction of the ζ potential effected by the opposing ions holds for the alkali ions. This destruction of the double layer may, however, as in the present case, also be due to the formation of a definite compound between the added ions and the ions which give the colloidal particles their charge.

6. Peptization

We have, up to the present, looked upon the possession of an electric charge by the colloidal particle as an accomplished fact, but we will now consider this matter further.

If a solution of silver nitrate and one of a halide are allowed to flow into each other, the silver halide is formed ; for example,

$$AgNO_3 + KI = AgI + KNO_3.$$

According to the investigations of Lottermoser, the silver iodide precipitates if approximately equivalent quantities of the salt are mixed. If the silver nitrate is in excess the silver iodide remains in colloidal suspension, the particles being positively charged. If the potassium iodide is in excess, the silver iodide again remains in colloidal suspension, but this time the particles are charged negatively.

The potassium iodide or the silver nitrate are said to peptize the sol. The presence of such a peptizing agent is a necessary condition for the existence of the sol.

It has long been known that a perfectly pure substance cannot be colloidally dispersed in pure water ; a small amount of an electrolyte is always necessary. If, for example, silver is colloidally dispersed by breaking it down into minute particles under water in an electric arc, the addition of some alkali to the water is essential for the formation of a good sol.

If the traces of peptizing electrolyte are removed by dialysis, the sol coagulates. This, for example, is what takes place if a ferric oxide sol is made by the following reaction :

$$2FeCl_3 + 3H_2O \rightarrow Fe_2O_3 + 6HCl \text{ (by warming)}$$

and is then dialysed for a long time. The sol coagulates in the dialyser.

The explanation of the peptizing effect of very small traces of an electrolyte will be clear if we remember our discussion on p. 128.

If a sol is to exist then the R curve—the repulsion curve in Fig. 49 (p. 128)—must be sufficiently high for the repulsion energy to exceed the kinetic energy (E_b greater than $\frac{3}{2} kT$). The R curve lies higher the greater the ζ potential. If there is to be a ζ potential at all, there must first be a double layer with a certain ϵ potential, and this owes its existence alone to the potential-determining ions and the opposing ions. In pure water, or rather in the saturated solution of the colloidally dispersed substance (which is always very slightly soluble), the ϵ potential is too low to give rise to a sufficient ζ potential to stabilize the sol (see p. 129). The potential difference of the double layer increases, however, when one of the potential-determining ions is added. This can thus peptize the colloid, and its removal by dialysis causes on the contrary a decrease in ϵ and ζ. For a silver iodide sol the iodide ion is therefore a peptizing agent (see p. 87; its addition lowers the silver ion concentration). For the ferric oxide sol, which, for the sake of convenience, we will call $Fe(OH)_3$, the hydrogen ion (which decreases the hydroxyl ion concentration in the intermicellar liquid) is the peptizing ion. For the arsenious sulphide sol, the sulphide ion, S^{--}, acts in this way. The terms "potential-determining ion" and "peptizing ion" are thus very closely related.

However, the added ion is not always the proper peptizing ion, as we may regard the ion which forms the inner component of the double layer. In the case of stannic oxide, SnO_2 (see p. 133), we saw in the preceding section that the addition of caustic potash gives rise to chemical reaction with the exterior of the particle, whereby a stannic oxide molecule on the outside of the particle becomes converted into a potassium stannate, K_2SnO_3, molecule, the ions of which form the double layer. In this case, then, the double layer arises because of the existence on the boundary surface of an ionized compound. Similar cases of peptization by chemical action on the outside of the particle are probably found also in connection with the above-mentioned ferric oxide sol, which, under the influence of the peptizing agent, hydrochloric acid, may give rise to hydrated ferric ions on the surface of the particles, balanced by an atmosphere of chloride ions.

For substances with a simple crystal structure the peptizing process is particularly easy to visualize. We take as an example the silver iodide sol, for which we have already seen that excess of potassium iodide gives rise to a peptized sol which is negatively charged, and excess of silver nitrate to a positively charged sol.

Fig. 53 represents a section of the crystal lattice of silver iodide. The black dots are silver ions, the white ones iodide ions. It is seen that each silver ion has as nearest neighbours six iodide ions, four in the

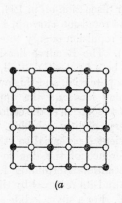

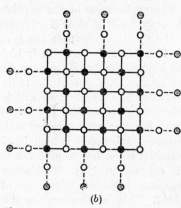

(a)   (b)

FIG. 53.

plane of the paper, one in front of, and one behind the paper. For a silver ion on the surface of the crystal, however, one of these iodide ions is missing. It is therefore obvious that if the crystal is placed in a solution of potassium iodide, it will try to attract an iodide ion into the vacant place of the missing sixth iodide ion. The adsorbed iodide ion thus gives each particle a negative charge and potassium ions from the solution act as " counter-ions " to complete the double layer, as shown in Fig. 53.

Had we an excess of silver nitrate in place of potassium iodide, the iodide ions would have attracted silver ions from the solution, and reasoning completely analogous to the above indicates that a positively charged sol would result.

These considerations, which are due to Mukherdjee and to Fajans, give us some idea of how the double layer may arise in the case of crystalline substances.

7. Form of the Particles

Throughout the preceding work it has been tacitly assumed that the colloidal particles are spherical, or approximately so. This is actually often the case, but there may be considerable deviations which are made clearly evident by the optical properties of the sols. In fact, ultramicroscopic investigation shows that, in the case of vanadium pentoxide sols, for example, the particles are long and needle-shaped. The sol at rest shows no peculiarities, but if it is made to flow through a tube the needles orient themselves in the direction of flow and the sol shows double refraction. The ferric oxide sol, which is composed of flat plates, also shows double refraction under these conditions. It can be said in general that all sols with anisometric particles show this phenomenon (it is often visible on stirring). It has been shown that parallel oriented anisometric particles give rise to double refraction ; if the particles are themselves doubly refracting crystallites the phenomenon is more marked.

During the last ten years or so, the electron microscope (Chapter VI, § 4) has provided much direct information about the size and shape of colloidal particles. In this instrument a beam of electrons is used instead of visible light, and in favourable cases particles of dimensions as small as 15 Å. have been made visible. The method is particularly easy to apply in the case of inorganic colloids ; it has been shown, for instance, that the particles in a vanadium pentoxide sol are thread-like, while those in a ferric oxide sol are disc-shaped. Recent developments in technique have also made it possible to obtain much valuable information about organic colloids, such as virus particles. For further details see Alexander and Johnson's *Colloid Science* or Kruyt's *Colloid Science,* where actual photographs are given.

K 2

CHAPTER VIII

HYDROPHILIC COLLOIDS

1. Introduction

AMONG lyophilic colloids, hydrophilic colloids deserve special mention, on the one hand because all biocolloids belong to this class, and on the other because hydrophilic colloids are almost always electrically charged, a phenomenon which does not often occur with macromolecules in other dispersion media.

The electrical charge of hydrophilic colloids is indicated by the fact that they conduct electricity and show electrophoresis. Moreover, the viscosity of these colloids is strongly influenced by electrical phenomena. The charge is chiefly due to the dissociation of certain groups in the molecule, such as —COOH, —SO_3H, —POH, —NH_2, etc. Since a single macromolecule may have many of these dissociable groups they may also be called *polyelectrolytes*.

2. Electrical Behaviour. The Electroviscous Effect

It is impossible to study the electrical behaviour of hydrophilic colloids under the ultramicroscope because the particles are not made visible in that instrument (see p. 119). For the determination of electrophoretic velocity it is necessary to use an arrangement such as the electrophoresis apparatus developed by the Swedish physical chemist Tiselius some twenty years ago, which is a much improved version of the simple arrangement (see pp. 108–110). With the Tiselius apparatus, elaborate arrangements are made to ensure stable and reproducible boundaries between the colloidal solution and the dispersion medium, and the boundaries are observed by an optical method depending on differences of refractive index. With this apparatus, it is possible to identify and separate the various components of a mixed colloidal solution by taking advantage of their varying electrophoretic mobilities. This is especially useful for solutions of proteins, and the Tiselius apparatus, which is obtainable commercially, is now standard equipment in all laboratories concerned with any aspect of protein chemistry. For further details of this technique see, for instance, Alexander and Johnson's *Colloid Science*.

There is, however, another method of investigating the electrical state of the particles.

Fig.. 54 shows the effect of the addition of an electrolyte to an agar solution on its viscosity. The concentration of the electrolyte in gm.

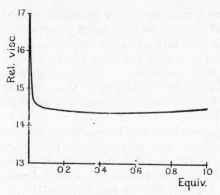

FIG. 54.

equiv. per litre is represented on the x-axis, and the relative viscosity, η_s/η_0, on the y-axis. It will be noticed that the effect is very marked for small concentrations, but that after a certain concentration is reached the further addition of electrolyte produces very little effect on the viscosity. This marked effect for small concentrations at once brings to mind the effect on electrokinetic phenomena (Chapter V).

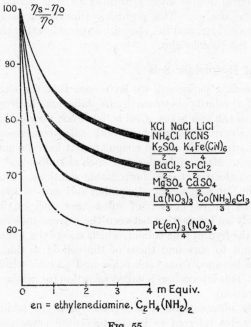

FIG. 55.

This impression is strengthened by an examination of Fig. 55, which shows the initial portions of the viscosity curves for various added electrolytes. All salts with univalent cations lower the ζ potential of the agar particles to almost the same extent, so that the curves all crowd together in the black line. Similarly there is only one line for divalent ions, and one for trivalent ions. One tetravalent ion was used in the course of the investigation, and the curve for it falls below the rest, as would be expected.

This effect of electrolytes can be readily explained if it is assumed that we are concerned here with a double layer phenomenon. It is obvious that the existence of a double layer will increase the viscosity while its compression by the addition of salts will decrease the viscosity. The increase in viscosity due to the electrical charge is called the *electroviscous effect.*

The electroviscous effect can be explained in most cases by the effect of the electric charge on the shape of the polyelectrolyte particles. Polyelectrolytes are often chain molecules, or they consist of branched chains. In solution they form relatively loose tangled clumps. If the tangled molecule is charged by electrolytic dissociation the individual charge sites repel each other and the tangle swells up, giving rise to increased viscosity. On increasing the content of electrolyte, however, an electrical double layer is formed at each charge site, which screens off the charge. The repulsion thus becomes smaller, the tangles become tighter, and the viscosity approaches that characteristic of uncharged macromolecules.

3. Stability of Hydrophilic Sols

In the preceding paragraph we have seen that the electric charge is a point of similarity between hydrophilic and hydrophobic sols. The stability of the two types of sol is, however, very different. Small quantities of electrolytes, which in both cases compress the double layer, cause hydrophobic sols to coagulate but have no such effect on hydrophilic sols. Macromolecules, too, such as rubber and polystyrene which have no electric charge, form stable solutions. This solubility of hydrophilic (more generally, lyophilic) sols can be explained in a similar way to the dissolution of substances with small molecules. There is clearly an interaction between the solvent molecules and the molecules of the hydrophilic colloid, which makes the molecules of the solvent attempt to surround those of the colloid so that the colloid molecules are loosened from each other and go into solution as individual units. This interaction is called solvation (or, where water is the solvent, hydration).

From these observations it is evident that, in addition to the envelope of water referred to in the preceding paragraph, the agar particles also possess an electric charge which is entirely similar to that possessed by hydrophobic sols. We have seen on p. 140 that the addition of small quantities of electrolytes to hydrophilic sols does not bring about complete coagulation, although we have just found that the addition of electrolytes does diminish the ζ potential of the particle or even removes it. Hydrophilic sols are therefore protected from coagulation not only by their electrical double layer, but at the same time by another factor which is more or less independent of the ζ potential.

It may be assumed that the other protecting factor is the envelope of water to which we have already referred. This assumption can be tested by the following experiment. If approximately 50 wt. per cent. of absolute alcohol is added to an agar sol, it suddenly loses all its hydrophilic properties and becomes a hydrophobic sol. The viscosity becomes that of the dispersion medium (the mixture of alcohol and water). The particles give clear diffraction patterns in the ultramicroscope, and are seen to possess the Brownian motion. The sol shows the bluish appearance (Tyndall effect) which is characteristic of mastic and sulphur sols.

As is well known, alcohol is a strong dehydrating agent. The alcohol therefore appropriates the water which has been surrounding the agar particles as a water envelope. The agar particles, bereft of this sheath of water, do not differ at all from the particles of a hydrophobic sol. If small quantities of an electrolyte are added to the sol in this condition it is immediately precipitated. If, conversely, an electrolyte is added to the agar sol, and then alcohol is added, the electro-viscous effect disappears as before, the ζ potential is removed, and coagulation occurs.

These observations show that the essential difference between a hydrophilic and a hydrophobic sol is the degree of interaction between the substance and the solvent, which in the case of the former is great, and for the latter is too weak for the substance to go into solution spontaneously. The terms *reversible* and *irreversible* express the difference in external behaviour of the two types of colloid, while the terms *hydrophilic* and *hydrophobic* express the essential difference in internal structure.

4. Proteins

If protein sols, such as occur in living organisms, are investigated they are found to consist of electrically charged particles. It has been found that the electrical charge on protein sols is dependent to a large extent on whether the medium has an acid or an alkaline reaction ; in other words, the electrical charge of the particles depends on the hydrogen ion concentration of the surroundings, i.e. on the pH.

It is important to understand the reasons for this. Proteins, as is well known, are built up of amino-acids. Each protein molecule has many —COOH and —NH₂ groups which means that it can function both as an acid and as a base. In an alkaline medium (NaOH) the carboxyl groups are dissociated (—COO⁻, Na⁺) and the —NH₂ groups are un-ionized. The protein is then negatively charged. In acid medium (HCl) on the other hand, the ionization of the carboxyl group is strongly repressed, but the amino group is ionized (—NH₃⁺, Cl⁻) so that the protein is positively charged. The charge can be demonstrated by means of the Tiselius electrophoresis apparatus, by means of which proteins can be analysed and separated quantitatively even though there are comparatively small differences of charge between them.

The acidic and basic strength of an amino-acid molecule are in general not very great. Normally the acid character predominates, i.e. the tendency of the carboxyl groups to split off hydrogen ions is greater than that of the amino-radicals to give rise to hydroxyl ions. The amino-acids, therefore, are, generally speaking, acidic in nature.

A simple amino-acid, such as glycine, $H_2N.CH_2.COOH$, thus gives rise to three ions: $H_2N.CH_2.COO^-$, $^+H_3N.CH_2.COOH$, and $^+H_3N.CH_2.COO^-$ (a so-called "Zwitter" ion). We know that the following relationship exists between the concentration of the hydrogen and hydroxyl ions :

$$[H^+][OH^-] = K_w$$

If the dissociation constant of the amino-acid as an acid is K_a, and that as a base is K_b, the following three equations must hold for a solution of an amino-acid

$$[H^+][OH^-] = K_w \qquad \frac{[^+NH_3RCOO^-][H^+]}{[^+NH_3RCOOH]} = K_a$$

$$\frac{[^+NH_3RCOO^-][OH^-]}{[NH_2RCOO^-]} = K_b$$

Depending on the pH of the medium, which we can regulate by the addition of acid, or base, or buffer solutions, the equilibrium between H^+ ions, OH^- ions, and amino-acid ions can be altered. The concentration for which, $[^+NH_3.R.COOH] = [NH_2.R.COO^-]$, is called the isoelectric point of the amino-acid.

For proteins these equilibria occur at the surface of the particles. Thus the sign of the charge on the particle depends on whether the protein ion at a given hydrogen ion concentration gives rise to more

—COO⁻ ions or more —NH₃⁺ ions, when the particles will be negatively or positively charged, respectively (Fig. 56 *a*, *b*). At the isoelectric point as many cations as anions occur at the surface and the particle appears to be uncharged.

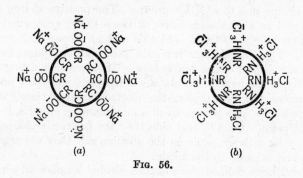

(a) (b)

FIG. 56.

The special behaviour of a protein compared with that of a polyelectrolyte with only one kind of dissociating group, is a consequence of its amphoteric nature ; it can act as a cation or an anion according to the pH of the medium.

The investigations of Loeb show that the viscosity of a gelatin sol varies with the hydrogen ion concentration of the medium in the manner shown by the curve in Fig. 57. The abscissæ are the hydrogen ion exponents of the medium, the ordinates are viscosities. As can be seen, the viscosity is a minimum at about pH 4·7, which is in fact the

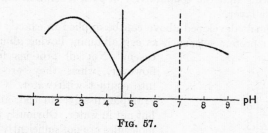

FIG. 57.

isoelectric point for gelatin, at which the electrophoretic mobility is zero. Thus the electroviscous effect arises—like the phenomenon of electrophoresis—as a direct result of the electrical double layer and the ζ potential.

When dealing with electrokinetic phenomena (p. 112) we saw that such a charging effect never goes on indefinitely but reaches a maximum value, and then begins to fall. We observe the same thing happening in Fig. 57, where the two branches of the curve which rise from the isoelectric point both reach a maximum value and then begin to fall. Suppose, for instance, we add hydrochloric acid, to convert all the —COO⁻ groups to —COOH, and leave the particles with a positive charge due to —NH₃⁺ groups. The positive charge on the particles will be a maximum when all the —COO⁻ groups have thus been converted to —COOH, and this sets an upper limit to the ζ potential. The chloride ions from the acid will, of course, form the " atmosphere " part of the double layer. If excess acid is now added, the density of the ionic atmosphere will increase, and the ζ potential will therefore fall. Naturally, the electrophoretic velocity of the gelatin molecules also goes through a maximum on either side of the isoelectric point. On the acid side they are positively charged, and migrate to the cathode, while on the alkaline side they are negatively charged, and migrate to the anode.

Similarly, Loeb defined the so-called alcohol number which is the number of c.c. of alcohol which must be added to the gelatin sol to cause coagulation. We have seen above that the action of the alcohol consists of a dehydration, i.e. in the removal of the water envelope which surrounds the particle, and is a factor governing its stability. We have seen also that the protein solution is stabilized both by hydration and by electrical repulsion. Thus for coagulation to occur the particles must be dehydrated the more vigorously the greater their charge. There is accordingly a minimum at the isoelectric point, when the alcohol number is plotted against pH (Fig. 58).

Fig. 58 also represents the dependence of the electrical conductivity on pH, showing that the conductivity of such a solution must be due to the double layer.

The argument developed above can be applied in exactly the same way to other protein sols, such as egg albumin, bovine albumin, and casein. Not all proteins form sols, however, when they are brought into contact with water. Casein, for example, dissolves in acids and alkalis, but not in water. Obviously the casein molecules are not sufficiently hydrated to give a stable sol unless the charge is considerable; this is brought about by using acid or alkali, whose pH will be far removed from the isoelectric point. Gelatin or egg albumin, on the other hand, are sufficiently hydrated to remain in solution at their isoelectric points.

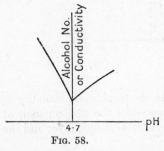

FIG. 58.

5. Salting Out

We have already noticed (p. 141) that it is, in general, necessary to add much greater concentrations of electrolyte to precipitate a hydrophilic sol than a hydrophobic one. We have also seen (p. 130) that for the removal of the charge on colloids only a few millimols of electrolyte are necessary. The larger quantity of electrolyte that has to be added in the case of hydrophilic colloids must play some other part, and it is obvious that this rôle must be that of a dehydrating agent.

If we compare the order in which the sodium salts of the following acids are effective in salting out, the series

$$SO_4 > \text{citrate} > \text{tartrate} > \text{acetate} > Cl > Br > NO_3$$

is obtained.

If the same effect is investigated, say, for the sulphates of different metals, the following series are obtained for univalent and bivalent cations, respectively :

$$Li > Na > K > Rb > Cs \text{ and } Mg > Ca > Ba.$$

We have already met lyotropic series of this kind, and we shall come across them again later (p. 163).

The lyotropic action of salts is related to the degree with which the ions combine with water ; the stronger is the combining power of the added ion with water, the more readily does it withdraw water from the colloidal particles. It is thus clear that the lyotropic series of ions is the order of their dehydrating powers.

Thus when a protein is precipitated by the addition of ammonium sulphate, the first few milli-equivalents of the salt lower the ζ potential, while the further quantity added has a dehydrating action ; addition of the salt therefore results in the successive removal of the two stability factors of the protein sol.

6. Summary

We have seen in the preceding paragraph that hydrophilic sols differ from hydrophobic sols in that they are protected by hydration in addition to an electric charge. The latter is removed by electrolytes in just the same way as with hydrophobic sols. The water is removed by dehydrating agents, which may be either non-electrolytes, such as alcohol, or electrolytes, which are effective in the order of the lyotropic series.

In Fig. 59 the factors which govern the stability of a hydrophilic sol, and the methods by which they can be reduced and removed, are summarized.

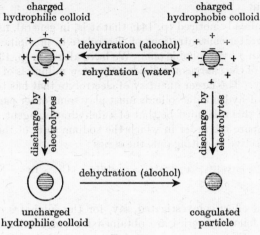

FIG. 59.

7. Coacervation

The scheme given in Fig. 59 is, however, too simple. There is a phenomenon which has not yet been mentioned, and which finds no place in the scheme. If the protecting potential and also the protecting water envelope are both gradually removed, there is an intermediate stage where liquid drops separate, which unite to form an oily layer. This phenomenon is called *coacervation*. The coacervation drops appear to be rich in colloid, whilst the remaining liquid, from which they have separated—the so-called equilibrium liquid—is poor in colloidal particles. Thus, after complete removal of the two stabilizing factors the colloid separates as a dry aggregate, but if the charge and the water layer are incompletely removed the colloid separates in such a manner that it forms a viscous liquid with its remaining water of hydration. Coacervation is thus a state intermediate between complete stability and flocculation, in which the colloidal particles retain their separate identity. If the liquid after, for example, partial dehydration with alcohol is diluted with water, the sol state is restored. The phenomenon is in fact usually observed as a half-way stage to complete precipitation.

A similar phenomenon occurs if we simply mix a positively charged hydrophilic sol and a negatively charged one. At pH 3·5, for example, gelatin is positively charged (as it is below the isoelectric point, pH 4·7) ; gum arabic is negatively charged. The latter is not a protein, and its charge is unaffected by change of pH. On mixing these two sols complex coacervation takes place, in which the droplets which separate contain particles of both colloids. Both types of particle retain their identity, as is shown by the fact that in an electric field the gelatin particles migrate to the cathode, and the gum arabic particles to the anode. Complex coacervation thus involves an electrical attraction between the two kinds of particles, but with complete coalescence prevented by hydration. Complex coacervation can sometimes be induced, if it does not occur as soon as the two colloids are mixed, by adding a small amount of a dehydrating agent such as alcohol in order to reduce the hydration.

Of course, complex coacervation can be hindered or stopped altogether by reducing the potential of at least one of the sols. Neutral salts thus stop complex coacervation, and since it is immaterial which of the two sols loses its electrical protection (coacervation, of course, is due to opposition in charges), both anions and cations are effective. Neutral salts are therefore effective in the following order :

$$Al^{+++} > Ba^{++} > K^{+}$$

and, for anions, in the order

$$Fe(CN)_6^{---} > SO_4^{--} > Cl^-.$$

Multivalent ions are in a position to bring about coacervation with a given colloid if this has a charge opposite to that of the ion. Thorium nitrate, $Th(NO_3)_4$, brings about coacervation with gum arabic. It appears that each Th^{++++} ion only presents one of its valencies to the micelle, so that only one of the negative charges of the latter is neutralized ; the other three positive charges are turned to the outside of the micelle. The opposite charge which thus arises on the surface of the micelle obviously gives rise to a phenomenon which is completely analogous to that of complex coacervation. It is called *auto-complex coacervation*. Electrical separation is observed, and the effect of neutral salts is just the same as has been described above for ordinary complex coacervation.

8. Protective Action

A characteristic property of some hydrophilic colloids remains to be dealt with. It is the protective action against coagulation by electrolytes that these hydrophilic colloids have on hydrophobic ones. If a certain quantity of an electrolyte is added to a gold sol, the sol coagulates, as appears from the fact that the colour of the sol, originally red, changes to blue. If, however, a very small quantity of gelatin is added to the sol initially, the same quantity of electrolyte is no longer able to bring about coagulation. This protective action is a specific property of various proteins, and may be used for their recognition. The number of milligrams of the hydrophilic colloid which is just sufficient to prevent the coagulation of 10 c.c. of gold sol prepared in a specified way when 1 c.c. of a 10 per cent. solution of sodium chloride is added is called the *gold number*.

Thus, for gelatin, the gold number is 0·005, for casein 0·01, for gum arabic 0·15, and for dextrin about 10. The strongly protective action of gelatin on the one hand contrasts markedly with the weak action of dextrin on the other.

This protective action can be explained by the fact that the gold particles adsorb gelatin particles strongly. The gold particles thus become protected not only by their electric charges, but also by the hydration of the gelatin particles, so that on collision with other particles coagulation does not take place. The protective colloid thus imparts its extra stability factor to the protected particle.

Gelatin and proteins exert this protective action, however, only with *alkaline* gold sols. Acidic gold sols are not protected ; in fact, the gelatin in this case acts as a very effective coagulant. The concentrations for which different proteins bring about the coagulation of a gold sol—the so-called U numbers (precipitation numbers)—are just as characteristic as the numbers expressing their protective action. Because the gold sol in an acid medium is probably close to its critical potential, and the gelatin has an opposite charge to that of the gold sol, mutual coagulation occurs.

CHAPTER IX

MACROMOLECULAR COLLOIDS

1. Introduction

In this chapter we give a further discussion of colloidal solutions in which the particles are single large molecules ; in general these are lyophilic colloids. These substances include such natural products as rubber, carbohydrates and proteins ; these were long suspected of having very large molecules, but reliable methods for the determination of molecular weights in this range have been developed only recently. Apart from such natural colloids, many high polymers have been made during the last thirty years, the size of whose molecules brings them into the colloidal range.

2. Macromolecules

Let us take styrene, $C_6H_5 . CH{=}CH_2$, or phenyl-ethylene, as an example. Its formula may be written shortly as $R . CH{=}CH_2$. This unsaturated hydrocarbon is a liquid at ordinary temperatures, but polymerizes on keeping, becoming more and more viscous as the polymerization proceeds. If the freshly prepared liquid is dissolved in an organic liquid, such as benzene, it can be shown cryoscopically that the substance is dissolved in the form of single molecules. If the styrene is allowed to stand, polymerization occurs, and very soon very large molecules are present. By polymerization under the correct conditions, degrees of polymerization of 100, 1000, and even of 6000 times the original have been reached. (This is expressed by saying $P = 100$, $P = 1000$, etc.) Such a macromolecule is a long chain of the type

$$-RCH-CH_2-RCH-CH_2-RCH-CH_2-RCH-CH_2-$$

Macromolecular substances can arise not only from polymerization, but also by continued condensation. As an example we may take the condensation of glycerol ($CH_2OH . CHOH . CH_2OH$; represented schematically as o-o-o) with succinic acid ($COOH . CH_2 . CH_2 . COOH$; represented as O—O) with elimination of water and the formation of an ester. This gives rise to

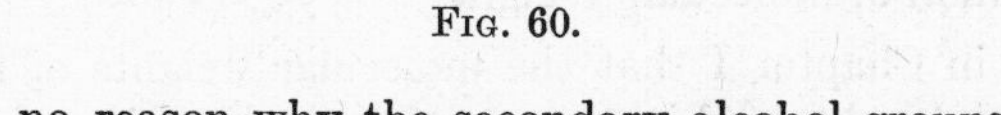

FIG. 60.

but there is no reason why the secondary alcohol groups should not also react.

In this second case the molecule will extend in two or perhaps three dimensions, and thus will be more compact than the chain molecule shown in Fig. 60. This also occurs in the case of bakelite, the product of repeated condensation of phenol and formaldehyde.

These large molecules are of colloidal dimensions. The length of a small molecule will be reckoned in Ångstrom units, and might be about Å., or 0·3 mμ. If, then, a chain molecule is built up from 100 small molecules, the chain will be about 30 mμ long. (This is supposing the chain to be fully extended ; in fact, such chains are often coiled up.) To make a spherical molecule with a diameter of 30 mμ would, of course, require many more simple molecules, of the order $P = 10^6$. The molecular weight of the chain molecule if we suppose that of the simple molecule to be 200 would thus be 20,000, and that of the spherical molecule would be of the order 2×10^8. Such molecules are therefore of colloidal dimensions and do actually behave as colloids. For instance, they have a very small velocity of diffusion.

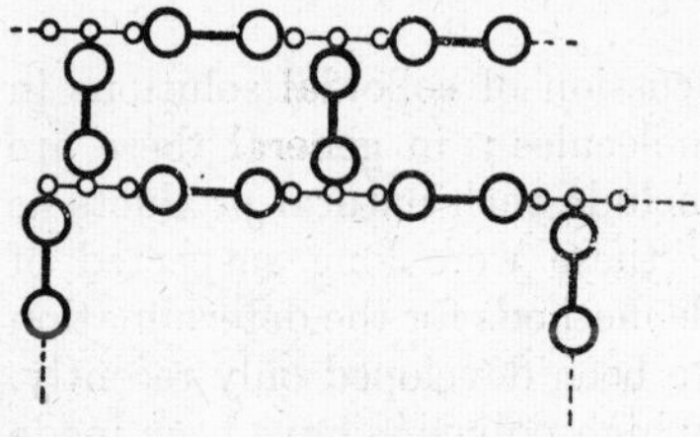

FIG. 61.

It ought, however, to be said that the course of these polymerization and condensation reactions should not be formalized too much, as though at any given instant the polymer consists purely of molecules of one degree of polymerization, say $P = 100$, or $P = 1000$. It must be understood that simultaneous reactions take place, and it is only possible to speak of a mean degree of polymerization, $\overline{P}$. Of course, it is possible to " fractionate " the reaction mixture to some degree by using the fact that the different polymerization products usually have different solubilities ; but this fractionation cannot be carried to such an extent that a " pure " product results. There is always a certain degree of spreading on either side of the principal constituent of any given fraction.

Two types of macromolecular colloid can be distinguished—chain colloids and branched colloids (also called linear and network colloids, respectively).

The question now arises, how may the molecular weight of a macromolecular substance be determined, and how can we find out if it is a chain or a network colloid ?

3. Determination of Molecular Weight

We learnt in Chapter I that the molecular weights of non-volatile substances can be obtained by determining the lowering of the freezing point, or the elevation of the boiling point or the osmotic pressure.

For macromolecular substances, which, of course, contain comparatively few molecules per unit weight, and of which, in consequence, solutions of only very small molecular concentrations can be made, we very soon reach the limits of possibility of cryoscopic and ebullioscopic measurements, as explained on p. 124.

Modern methods of measuring osmotic pressures are sufficiently precise to give fairly accurate values for the molecular weights of high polymers (see p. 124). Another important group of methods uses the sedimentation of the colloidal particles under the influence of the very high gravitational fields obtainable with the ultra-centrifuge (see p. 120). In this latter connection, either the sedimentation equilibrium can be measured, or the velocity of sedimentation can be observed. The technique is a difficult one (for details see, e.g. Alexander and Johnson) but can yield information about molecular shapes as well as about molecular weights. However, a completely different method of investigation—the viscometric method—will now be considered.

4. Viscometry of Macromolecular Colloids

With the help of solubility and streaming experiments we can easily discover whether we are dealing with a network or with a chain colloid. A chain colloid can usually be dissolved in a suitable solvent and a more or less viscous solution is obtained. A network colloid, which to all intents and purposes is one very large molecule, does not dissolve. At the most it swells when placed in a solvent (or rather a swelling medium) because the latter penetrates into the spaces of the network. The swollen colloid is a *gel*, of which the properties will be more fully dealt with in Chapter XI. The study of the viscosity of solutions of chain molecules sheds light on their form and size.

Einstein showed in 1905 that the viscosity of a disperse system is very simply related to the viscosity of the dispersion medium, viz.,

$$\eta_S = \eta_0 \left(1 + k\phi \right) \quad . \quad . \quad . \quad . \quad . \quad (1)$$

where η_S is the viscosity of the sol, η_0 is that of the solvent, k is a constant and ϕ is the total volume of the dispersed particles as a fraction of the volume of the sol. This equation only holds with accuracy when the volume of the particles is small with respect to the total volume, and the particles must be large compared with the molecules of the dispersion medium. The first condition can usually be satisfied by extrapolating the curve of viscosity against dilution to large dilutions. The second condition is generally fulfilled by lyophobic sols and to a fair approximation by lyophilic sols. The constant k depends on the form of the particles but not on their size. For massive spherical particles k is 2·5, for oblong or disc-shaped particles it is always greater than 2·5. In other words, the viscosity does not depend on the degree of dispersion of the colloid, but on the relative volume, for a given form.

Experiments with models (glass balls dispersed in salt solution) and with various hydrophobic sols have supported Einstein's formula.

In the case of chain colloids there are definite deviations. The constant k, which is in this case much greater than 2·5, now depends strongly on the size of the particles, i.e. on the degree of polymerization, $\overline{P}$. For low values of $\overline{P}$, where the determination of the size of the molecule is still possible by osmotic methods, k has been shown to vary directly with the chain length, and therefore with $\overline{P}$. At higher degrees of polymerization

$$\eta_s = \eta_0 \, (1 + k\overline{P}^\alpha\phi) \quad . \quad . \quad . \quad . \quad . \quad (2)$$

where α lies between 0·5 and 1. This formula may also be written

$$\frac{\eta \; - \eta_0}{\eta_0 c} = k\overline{P}^\alpha . \quad . \quad . \quad . \quad . \quad . \quad (3)$$

where c is the concentration in weight per cent. and k and α are constants which depend not on the degree of polymerization, but to some extent on the nature of the polymer and the solvent.

The quantity $\dfrac{\eta_s - \eta_0}{\eta_0 c}$, which is often written as $[\eta]$, is called the " viscosity number." It denotes the contribution of each weight per cent. of dispersed substance to the increase of viscosity.

With the help of equation (3) the degree of polymerization of a chain colloid can be calculated, if the values of k and α are determined beforehand by experiments with polymers of known degree of polymerization.

It is interesting to discuss why long chain molecules give solutions of much higher viscosity than short ones.

In the first place it is necessary to consider solvation, i.e. the linking of solvent molecules to the dispersed substance. This solvation would have the effect of increasing the volume of the dispersed substance and could thus provide an explanation of the higher viscosity. It is, however, not probable that solvation would change with degree of polymerization ; as the molecule becomes larger, the basic molecule is built on to, and solvation is fixed by the type of atom present and their mutual arrangement, which does not vary greatly on polymerization.

We must therefore seek elsewhere an explanation of the effect of degree of polymerization on viscosity. We must first have a clear picture in our minds of what a chain molecule is like. In fact, the macromolecule may have an extended form (actually a zig-zag, since the angle between the carbon valencies is 109° rather than 180°) or it may be tangled up. Since there is free rotation about single bonds, such molecules in solution are likely to spend most of their time in coiled-up configurations.

Such a tangle, of course, gives rise to a much greater ϕ than the volume of the dry material of the dispersed particle alone, even if solvation is taken into account ; and the longer the chain the " thicker " the tangle. So we see that $\dfrac{\eta_s - \eta_0}{\eta_0 c}$ must increase with the length of the chain (and therefore with the degree of polymerization, $\overline{P}$).

That a chain colloid forms tangles and not straight rods is also shown by the following observation. We have seen on p. 137 that rod-shaped particles, such as occur in vanadium pentoxide sol, V_2O_5, show double refraction when the sol is streaming. Rod-like molecules should show this effect to a very great extent ; yet, in fact, these chain colloids show it hardly at all. That the effect occurs even to a very small degree is probably due to the fact that the tangles tend, in streaming, to become to some extent flatter, and so they acquire a slightly anisotropic form.

5. Biocolloids

From the work outlined in the above paragraphs we obtain a deeper insight into the structure of biocolloids. As examples we may choose first of all the glucosidic polysaccharides, beginning with cellulose. This compound gives cellobiose as an intermediate product, and glucose as the final product, on hydrolysis. The structures of glucose and cellobiose are as follows :

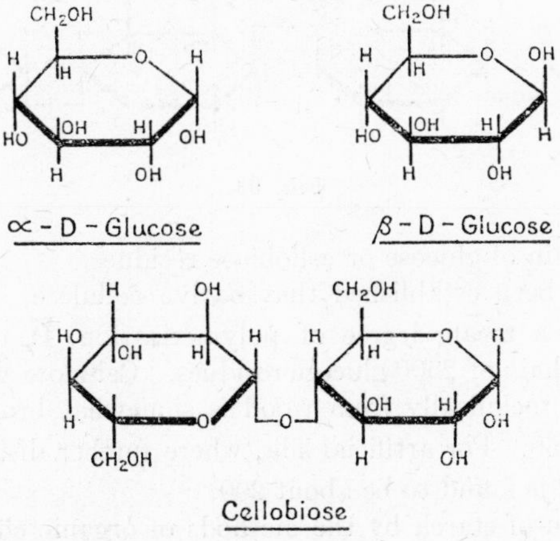

α - D - Glucose   β - D - Glucose

Cellobiose

FIG. 62.

Glucose, as shown, has a ring of five carbon atoms and one oxygen, the plane of which is supposed to be at right angles to the plane of the paper ; the other atoms and groups are attached above and below the plane of the ring. Cellobiose is a disaccharide, whose molecule consists of two glucose molecules linked together by the elimination of a molecule of water.

Now, cellulose itself is not readily brought into colloidal solution ; it passes more readily into the colloidal state if certain modifications are made in the molecule. The best known of these is that produced by treatment with sodium hydroxide and carbon disulphide, when the following change in the CH_2OH group takes place :

$$-CH_2OH + NaOH \rightarrow -CH_2ONa + H_2O$$

$$-CH_2ONa + CS_2 \rightarrow CH_2OC \diagdown^{SNa}_{S}$$

The latter substance is a xanthogenate and dissolves in alkalis giving the so-called viscose of the artificial silk industry.

Another method is the esterification of the hydroxyl groups. With nitric acid (and sulphuric acid) nitrocellulose is obtained, which dissolves in a mixture of alcohol and ether. With acetic anhydride (and sulphuric acid) cellulose acetate is obtained, which dissolves in acetone.

Viscometric observations according to § 4 with these dissolved cellulose derivatives show that we are dealing with a chain molecule to which the following formula (supported also by other investigations) must be given :

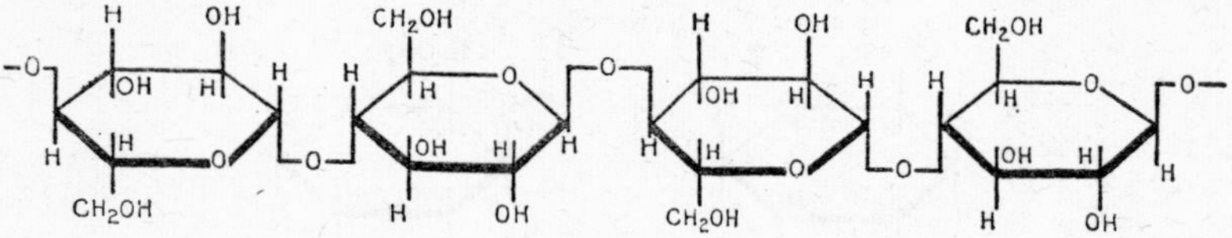

FIG. 63.

i.e., a long chain of glucose or cellobiose residues.

It has also been established that native cellulose, such as occurs in cotton, has a mean degree of polymerization, $\overline{P}$, of 2500, i.e. it consists of a chain of 2500 glucose residues. Cellulose which has been manufactured technically from wood is somewhat broken down and has $\overline{P}$ about 250. For artificial silk, where further disintegration has taken place, $\overline{P}$ is found to be about 200.

Investigation of starch by the methods of organic chemistry shows that here the breakdown product is not cellobiose but maltose.

Viscometric measurements show, moreover, that the chain is not straight but branched. Glycogen, which is also built up from glucose residues, probably is more extensively branched.

Many other biocolloids form similar macromolecules, some of them unbranched, some of them with branched chains. Pectin, for example, appears to have the methyl ester of galacturonic acid as the basic molecule, rubber is a polymer of isoprene, etc.

Proteins also are macromolecular colloids. Although from the viewpoint of organic chemistry proteins are made up of chain molecules (chains of amino-acids) they exist in two well-defined forms with regard to their solutions. In native proteins the polypeptide chains are folded to form compact spherical or oblong particles which give rise, in solution, to only a comparatively small increase in viscosity. By thermal treatment, addition of acids, alkalis or other chemicals, and in some cases merely by dilution, the protein becomes denatured, and the viscosity is increased. This means that the denatured proteins show the properties of chain molecules and take in solution the tangled form.

Molecular weights of proteins vary from about 15,000 up to about 500,000 and over, as has been shown in particular by experiments with the ultra-centrifuge. The whole question of protein structure is, however, a very rapidly developing field, which it would not be profitable to explore in the small amount of space available in this chapter.

CHAPTER X

COLLOIDAL ELECTROLYTES

In addition to the macromolecules dealt with in Chapters VIII and IX, there is yet another type of reversible colloid, namely the *colloidal electrolyte* or *associated colloid*. The principal representatives of this class are the soaps. By virtue of their chemical structure and also from their behaviour in very dilute solution these substances are known to have a comparatively low molecular weight. Sodium oleate, for example, has a molecular weight of 304, whilst the molecular weights of macromolecules range from 10,000 to more than 1,000,000.

The more concentrated solutions of soaps, however, show colloidal properties. The Tyndall effect is well marked, and diffusion is slow. In addition osmotic pressure and electrical conductivity indicate the presence of associated particles.

It is indeed unexpected that substances with a long paraffin chain and only one not very strong polar group dissolve so well in water.

These properties can be explained by supposing that in the concentrated soap solution micelles are formed. These consist of groups of 50 to 100 soap ions. The paraffin chains all lie to the inside of the micelle, and the polar, hydrophilic, ionized COO^- groups lie on the surface. The soap micelles thus have high negative charges. The alkali metal ions remain in the water and form the outer part of the double layer.

The formation of colloidal electrolytes, and of micelles, can be expected with substances with a large non-polar group (10 or more carbon atoms) and an ionized group. To this class belong the alkali metal salts of the higher fatty acids (the simple soaps) and the synthetic detergents which have, in place of the carboxyl group, a sulphonate or a sulphate group. It is also possible to have substances where the ionizable group is positively charged instead of negatively (e.g. the amino group), and so to have " cationic soaps " in which the micelle is positively charged.

These modern soaps have two additional advantages over the classical fatty acid salts. In the first place they are salts of strong acids, and hydrolysis does not occur ; they are " alkali-free." Then, the calcium and magnesium salts of most of the fatty acids used for making soaps are insoluble in water. The modern soaps, on the other hand, form soluble calcium and magnesium salts, and it is therefore possible to obtain a lather readily with hard water, or even in an acid medium, where the classical soaps would give a precipitate.

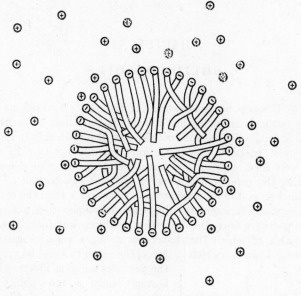

FIG. 64.

It is possible to explain many of the properties of soap solutions on the basis of this mixed polar-nonpolar (amphipolar) structure.

The nonpolar portion gives to the molecules a tendency to become concentrated in the liquid-air interface. There is thus positive adsorption, and the interfacial tension is lowered. This lower interfacial tension makes the increase of the surface area easier, and explains the lathering of soap solutions. Penetration into pores also becomes easier, and soaps are therefore good wetting agents. In washing, particles of a fatty or oily nature tend to become surrounded with soap ions. They thus acquire an electric charge on their exterior which repels the similar charge on the article to be washed and thus helps to loosen the particles.

In the living organism free fatty acid ions seldom occur. The bile acids, which are typical amphipolar substances with one carboxyl group to 24 carbon atoms, can form micelles, and behave in a manner quite analogous to the soaps. One of the functions which they fulfil in the process of digestion is to become adsorbed on fats, thus increasing the weight of and stabilizing fat droplets.

The phosphatides (e.g. lecithin) are built up in a similar way. They play an important part in natural membranes.

CHAPTER XI

SOLID COLLOIDS

1. Gelation

GELATIN dissolves in hot water. If the sol is allowed to cool it gradually becomes more viscous, and finally the whole becomes a solid mass, called a gel. Similar solid colloids can be obtained from lyophobic and lyophilic colloids which contain macromolecules. Silica and alumina sols form gels on addition of electrolytes, the determining factor being the valency of the ion of opposite sign to that of the sol, as explained on p. 130 for flocculation. Gelation is thus the result of a kind of coagulation where the dispersed substance does not separate as coarse particles from the dispersion medium, but forms a network in the spaces of which the dispersion medium remains caught up. Since these gels are very rich in water, the network must be very open, the particles hanging together by contact at only a few points ; the cohesion, or strength of the gel, is therefore small, much smaller than that of a crystal. We do not know exactly why certain sols form gels of this kind rather than coarse particles on coagulation. It is, however, understandable that anisotropic particles would particularly readily form gels (see Fig. 65a and b).

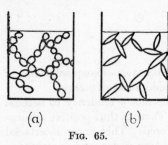

(a)   (b)

FIG. 65.

Silica gel has been very fully studied. It has been shown that the intermicellar spaces (the spaces in the network) have a cross-section of about 6 mμ.* The discontinuities in the gel are therefore much smaller than the wavelength of visible light and the silica gel is thus completely transparent (though it shows, of course, the Tyndall scattering, see pp. 118, 125).

2. Viscosity and Plasticity

In order to understand better the transition between sol and gel we must give a fuller account of viscosity, which up to now we have regarded as the inverse of the mobility of the liquid, which can be measured by the time required for a given volume of liquid to flow through a tube under a given (hydrostatic) pressure.

* Silica gel thus has a large " internal surface " ; see p. 91.

Newton showed that the velocity with which a liquid flows is directly proportional to the pressure under which the flow takes place. In Fig. 66 the velocity, v, is the ordinate and pressure, p, is the abscissa. According to Newton,

$$p = \eta v \text{ or } v = \frac{1}{\eta} \cdot p.$$

This coefficient of viscosity, η, is usually abbreviated to viscosity. It is clear from the figure that this coefficient is proportional to the tangent of the angle between the line in question and the v axis. In Fig. 66 examples are given of a liquid (I) with a very small viscosity (ether, for example), a liquid (II) with a medium viscosity (for example, water), and a liquid (III) with a high viscosity (for example, glycerol), and finally a liquid (IV) with a very high viscosity (for example, sealing wax, resin, asphalt).

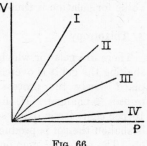

Fig. 66.

Many sols also behave as " Newtonian liquids," at least if they possess isometric particles ; but for the vanadium pentoxide sol, for example, where the particles are oriented in the direction of flow (see p. 137) the v-p diagram is not linear, but curved, as shown in Fig. 67,* curve I.

There are, of course, liquid systems which behave differently. Curve II of Fig. 67 is for a system where for small pressures there is no flow at all. It is necessary to exceed a certain pressure, f, (the "yield value "), before flow takes place. Examples of this type are all kinds of pastes, wet clay, etc. These substances are said to be plastic. Obviously there must be some internal bonds in these systems which have to be broken before flow will take place.

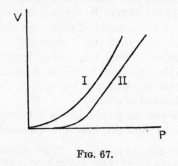

Fig. 67.

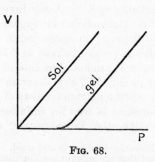

Fig. 68.

* Whether or not there is Newtonian flow is thus a distinguishing characteristic between chain and spherical colloids, as mentioned on p. 152. The tangles become flattened as they flow, the effect being greater the greater is the pressure.

In the case of gelation there is not a gradually increasing viscosity in the sense of Fig. 66, in which, say, the sol is represented by curve I, and the viscosity increases in the direction of curves II, III, and IV as the sol is converted into a gel. For the transformation from sol to gel a deformation of the curve takes place, as shown in Fig. 68. The sol is originally a Newtonian liquid. As gelation takes place the system shows a gradually increasing yield value.

In the previous paragraph we ascribed gel structure to a netlike structure with a few points of contact. The occurrence of a yield value for gelation is thus in good agreement with this view.

3. Thixotropy

There are gels for which the yield value is so small that by simply shaking the gel it is overcome. If at the same time the gelation takes place slowly the process is called thixotropy (*thixein* = shaking ; *tropein* = change). If, for example, an electrolyte is added to a 10 per cent. ferric oxide sol, it gels slowly. If the gel thus obtained is shaken the sol is produced, and gelation then begins afresh, and so on. The process can go on indefinitely.

Not only sols, but also coarse suspensions sometimes show thixotropy. For example, bentonite (an aluminium silicate) suspended in water is, to a large degree, thixotropic.

4. Gels of Macromolecular Colloids

A piece of unvulcanized rubber * is also a gel in the present sense, for it dissolves in benzene and then gives a sol. This sol is a dispersion of chain molecules built up of isoprene molecule units. The chain molecules appear to lie as mutually intertwining tangles in the gel. If the rubber is stretched in one direction, the molecules are pulled out straight, and become more or less parallel, a fact which has been shown remarkably well by X-ray investigations. While the original rubber gives no Debye-Scherrer diagram (see p. 126), stretched rubber gives a good diagram, in consequence of the fact that the " packets " of parallel molecules behave as " crystallites." Since they are no longer arranged at random, but now all lie in the direction of the pull, a somewhat modified X-ray diagram is obtained, which is called a fibre diagram (the pattern consists of arcs instead of circles).

The same is true for cellulose. We saw on p. 154 how a cellulose derivative, the xanthogenate, could be brought into the colloidal

---

* Vulcanized rubber is also a gel, but with different properties. This is due to the fact that the sulphur used in vulcanization adds on to the double bond in the isoprene molecules, forming bridges which bind together the chain molecules making a large open network. This picture gives a good explanation of the known mechanical properties which rubber acquires by vulcanization.

state. In the sol the molecules are dispersed in disordered tangles. In the manufacture of artificial silk the sol is forced through a narrow opening into a liquid, which regenerates the cellulose. As a result of the squirting the molecules become more or less stretched and directed. Thus crystallites arise again locally, and give a fibre diagram on X-ray analysis. Indeed the thread itself shows optical double refraction. Crystallites also occur in cellulose obtained from plants (cotton, wood).

Fig. 69a represents diagrammatically the state of disorder in the original structure, whilst Fig. 69b indicates what happens under the influence of an external directing force. In the latter diagram the arrows pointing to the bundled molecules indicate the crystallites. This state of affairs can also be described by saying that the gel consists

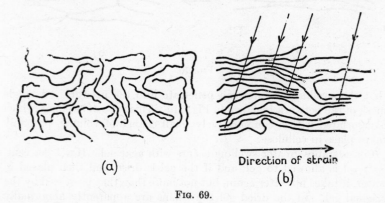

(a)

Direction of strain

(b)

FIG. 69.

of crystalline micelles, which are bound together by a fringe of projecting chain molecules.

The phenomenon of double refraction and the occurrence of fibre diagrams are also found for substances in living organisms (starch, muscle, etc.). It is therefore obvious that this type of structural investigation is of great importance in biology.

5. Swelling, Imbibition, and Syneresis

Swelling is the phenomenon in which a gel, when placed in a liquid, takes up so much of it that the volume of the gel markedly increases. If, for example, a piece of unvulcanized rubber is placed in benzene it swells more and more until it finally dissolves (unlimited swelling). If a gelatin gel is added to water, it takes up the liquid until it reaches a certain volume, after which it swells no further (limited swelling).

It is desirable in connection with the interaction between a gel and a liquid to make a distinction between imbibition and swelling. A freshly dried silica gel, of which the spaces in the network are filled with air, rapidly absorbs a liquid when immersed in it, in the fine capillary pores. The total volume, however, does not change. This is imbibition (*bibere* = to drink). The above-mentioned case of rubber is the other extreme of swelling ; obviously the benzene molecules push in between the chains of rubber molecules and thus make the gel swell. The affinity is so great that the benzene breaks down the mutual connection between the chain molecules and makes a sol.

There are, of course, many other cases between these two extremes. In the first place it is possible for the network in the dry gel to be closely packed, as in Fig. 70a, and on swelling it opens out (Fig. 70b) so

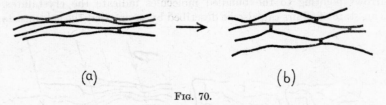

(a)   (b)

FIG. 70.

that the swelling medium can penetrate into the network. A single mesh of the network is shown in Fig. 71a. This type of swelling, which is associated with a comparatively small change of volume, probably takes place in cellulose.

Considerably greater swelling occurs with agar gel. If a 4 per cent. agar sol is allowed to gel, and if the gel is dried and then placed in water, it takes up water again, but not more than that possessed by the original gel. In the dried gel the chains are apparently abnormally strongly crinkled. As soon as the swelling agent is added, the chains try to become less crinkled by taking up the swelling agent. The cohesive forces between the knot points prevent further swelling (Fig. 71b).

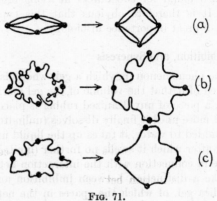

(a)

(b)

(c)

FIG. 71.

Then there are cases where the swelling does not stop when the gel has reached its original size, but proceeds further. Here the crinkles in the chain molecules are completely pulled out, and there is a tension in the network which becomes in equilibrium with the swelling force (Fig. 71c). This type of swelling takes place in concentrated gels with many knots and where there is a strong affinity between the swelling agent and the gel. Examples are the swelling of vulcanized rubber in benzene and the swelling of a 10 per cent. gelatin gel, obtained by gelatinization of a 10 per cent. gelatin sol in water.

The swelling of gelatin or of glue in water depends to a great extent on the pH of the medium ; it is least at the isoelectric point, and greatest in acid or alkaline solution. Thus, swelling is plainly connected with the degree of hydration, which is least at the isoelectric point, where the number of ionized groups is a minimum. Neutral salts influence swelling in the order of the lyotropic series.

$$SO_4^{--} < Cl^- < Br^- < NO_3^- < I^- < CNS^-$$
Swelling power increases

In addition to the general weakening influence of the electric effects, which oppose swelling, there is a specific effect connected with ionic hydration. The more strongly the ions themselves attach water (e.g. SO_4^{--}), the less they leave at the disposal of the swelling material.

The phenomenon of syneresis is, to a certain extent, the opposite of swelling. If an agar sol, for example, is allowed to gel a relatively massive block of gel is obtained. After some time, however, it is found that the gel has given up all its water ; the water is no longer linked to the gel. The exudation of this water is called syneresis. It must probably be ascribed to the fact that all possible nodal points have not been immediately formed in gelation, but gradually new ones form, resulting in a contraction of the gel and diminution of the intermicellar space. Water formerly present in the pores is forced out.

CHAPTER XII

SUPPLEMENT

IN this chapter we shall deal with some topics which were not included in our previous discussion because they could not be adequately considered without a knowledge of the facts learnt in the later chapters of the book.

1. The Donnan Membrane Equilibrium

A difficulty which arises in the determination of the osmotic pressure of a colloidal solution is that the colloid is never perfectly free from peptizing electrolytes (p. 135). Attempts have been made to overcome this difficulty by using parchment paper or collodion as the membrane. These are dialysing membranes (see p. 116), which allow electrolytes to pass through but not colloids. In this way, it might be thought, the osmotic pressure of the colloidal solution alone would be measured.

We shall see in what follows that this idea is quite wrong, and to study this point we shall choose a well investigated example, the determination of the osmotic pressure of congo red.

Congo red is the sodium salt of an aromatic sulphonic acid. The anion, however, is unable to diffuse through a parchment paper membrane (see p. 116). We thus have the case where the membrane is permeable to the cation but not to the anion.

The osmotic pressure of a mixture of congo red and sodium chloride solutions has been investigated on the basis of a theory due to Donnan. Consider this mixture in an osmometer and sodium chloride solution on the other side of the membrane. At first sight one would say that the sodium chloride, which can pass freely through the parchment membrane, should diffuse so that the same concentration of sodium chloride existed inside and outside, when equilibrium would be reached.

That this view is incorrect may be shown by the following considerations :

Let the solution inside the osmometer be indicated by i and that outside by o. Of course, detached ions cannot pass through the membrane. If they could, a sodium ion could escape from a chloride ion and strong electrical forces would be set up which would at once act against such an occurrence. We ask ourselves now what governs the probability that a sodium ion and a chloride ion from inside the osmometer should strike unit surface of the osmometer simultaneously. Recalling the treatment of Chapter II, it is clear that the probability is proportional to the product $[Na^+]_i \, [Cl^-]_i$. In a similar way, the chance that a sodium ion and a chloride ion from outside the osmometer should strike unit surface of the membrane at the same time is proportional to $[Na^+]_o [Cl^-]_o$. Also, we know (see Chapter I) that equilibrium can only be achieved when the same number of ions pass through the membrane in one direction as pass through it in the other in unit time, so that at equilibrium

$$[Na^+]_i [Cl^-]_i = [Na^+]_o [Cl^-]_o \quad . \quad . \quad . \quad . \quad . \quad (1)$$

We thus reach the conclusion that the product of the concentrations of Na^+ and Cl^- inside and outside the osmometer must be the same. Now, of course, the sodium ions inside the osmometer are provided not only by the sodium chloride, but also by the congo red, and this naturally introduces a complicating factor into the question of the concentrations of the various ions inside and outside the membrane.

Let us consider the state of affairs at the beginning of the experiment by a method which will be clear from the scheme below. In the diagram, symbols to the left of the line represent the ions present in the liquid within the osmometer, and those to the right of it the ions which exist outside the osmometer. We suppose that the solutions are so dilute that they may be assumed to be completely dissociated electrolytically, that the volume of liquid inside and outside is the same, and that the concentration of the congo red (represented by NaR) at the beginning of the experiment is c, that of the sodium chloride inside is c, and that of the sodium chloride outside is also c. The values have thus been chosen very arbitrarily for the sake of simplicity, this being only an example.

Na^+	R^-					Na^+	R^-		
c	c					c	c		
		Na^+	Cl^-	$\rightarrow$				Na^+	Cl^-
		c	c					$c+x$	$c+x$
Na^+	Cl^-					Na^+	Cl^-		
c	c					$c-x$	$c-x$		

On the basis of what has been stated above it is clear that at the beginning of the experiment there are too many sodium ions inside the osmometer. Sodium chloride must therefore pass through the membrane out of the instrument, and we will suppose that this happens until an amount has passed through corresponding to a concentration x, so that the final state is represented in the diagram to the right of the arrow.

This final state must be in agreement with equation (1) above. Hence

$$(2c - x)(c - x) = (c + x)^2$$
$$2c^2 - 3cx + x^2 = c^2 + 2cx + x^2$$
$$x = \tfrac{1}{5}c.$$

Hence there will be equilibrium when the sodium chloride concentration inside the osmometer is $\frac{4}{5}c$ and that outside is $\frac{6}{5}c$.

We can now calculate from these values how many solute particles there are inside and outside the membrane, and we find that inside there are 3·6 cN and outside 2·4 cN, where N is Avogadro's number (see p. 2).

If we had assumed that the sodium chloride played no part in the equilibrium because the membrane is permeable to it, we should obtain for the osmotic pressure the value

$$\pi = 2cRT$$

as given on p. 13. As it is, we know that at the final state of equilibrium there are 3·6 cN particles per unit volume inside and 2·4 cN particles per unit volume outside, so we reach the conclusion that the osmotic pressure, π, amounts to $1\cdot2cRT$.

Hence we find that the osmotic pressure according to Donnan's theory is 40 per cent. lower than that given by the straightforward application of van't Hoff's law.

If Donnan's theory is applied to the same osmometer system but with different concentrations of congo red and sodium chloride we find the results given in the table below :

No.	Original concentrations			Final state	
	NaR	NaCl on both sides of the membrane	Ratio	Per cent. NaCl$_i$	Ratio NaCl$_o$/NaCl$_i$
1	0·01	1	0·01	49·88	1·005
2	0·1	1	0·1	48·8	1·05
3	1	1	1	40	1·5
4	1	0·5	2	33	2
5	1	0·1	10	14·3	6
6	1	0·01	100	1·9	51

We see, from the last line of this table, that in this particular case the sodium chloride is almost entirely confined to the outer liquid. One would be led to believe, considering this example alone, that the membrane was impermeable to sodium chloride !

If the ratio between the osmotic pressure according to the usual van't Hoff law, and that given by Donnan's theory is calculated for the same systems as are given in the above table, the values given in the table following are obtained. The ratio of the concentrations only is given ; c_1 is the concentration of the congo red, and c_2 the total concentration of the sodium chloride. π_D and π_H are the osmotic pressures calculated according to Donnan's theory and the van't Hoff law, respectively.

No.	$\dfrac{c_2}{c_1}$	$\dfrac{\pi_D}{\pi_H}$
1	0·01	0·50
2	0·1	0·51
3	1	0·60
4	2	0·67
5	10	0·86
6	100	0·98

If the diffusible electrolyte has no ions in common with the colloidal electrolyte, exactly the same considerations apply, but in the final result it appears that the diffusible electrolyte has no effect on the observed osmotic pressure. For instance, let us now consider the scheme below, in which initially we have the sodium salt of congo red on one side of the membrane and potassium chloride on the other.

$$
\begin{array}{c|c|c}
\begin{array}{cc} \mathrm{Na^+} & \mathrm{R^-} \\ c_1 & c_1 \end{array} &
\begin{array}{cc} \mathrm{K^+} & \mathrm{Cl^-} \\ c_2 & c_2 \end{array} \rightarrow &
\end{array}
$$

$$
\begin{array}{cc|cc}
\mathrm{Na^+} & \mathrm{R^-} & \mathrm{K^+} & \\
c_1 - z & c_1 & c_2 - x & \\
\mathrm{K^+} & \mathrm{Cl^-} & \mathrm{Na^+} & \mathrm{Cl^-} \\
x & x - z & z & c_2 - x + z
\end{array}
$$

Applying the equation (1) on p. 165 we have

$$\frac{[\mathrm{Na^+}]_i}{[\mathrm{Na^+}]_o} = \frac{[\mathrm{Cl^-}]_o}{[\mathrm{Cl^-}]_i}$$

Since the same reasoning can be applied to the passage of $\mathrm{K^+}$ and $\mathrm{Cl^-}$ ions as for $\mathrm{Na^+}$ and $\mathrm{Cl^-}$ ions, we have

$$\frac{[\mathrm{Na^+}]_i}{[\mathrm{Na^+}]_o} = \frac{[\mathrm{Cl^-}]_o}{[\mathrm{Cl^-}]_i} = \frac{[\mathrm{K^+}]_i}{[\mathrm{K^+}]_o}$$

From the above it is seen that each of these ratios is equal to $\dfrac{c_1 + c_2}{c_2}$ and values of this fraction are given in the table below.

$\dfrac{c_1}{c_2}$	$\dfrac{c_1 + c_2}{c_2}$
1	2
10	11
100	101

The above theory can be applied to the explanation of a number of observations.

In the first place it should be mentioned that the conclusions drawn by Donnan are by no means confined to the above example, but apply in general whenever we have to do with ions separated by a membrane. Nor are they confined to substances which cannot pass through the membrane as is the case with congo red used in the above argument. Thus, whenever we have to do with an electrolyte (such as the NaR above) of which one ion attaches itself to a colloidal particle, unequal distribution of the electrolyte on the two sides of the membrane must occur.

A second conclusion follows immediately from this. All attempts to measure the osmotic pressure of colloids must give results distorted by this equilibrium, and the " molecular size " of particles cannot then be calculated by the simple van't Hoff equation.

From the table on p. 167 the osmotic pressure calculated by van't Hoff's equation agrees more closely with that calculated from Donnan's theory as the ratio of colloid to electrolyte is greater.

A third conclusion from the theory is as follows : it might be thought that an electrical potential difference would exist between a reversible electrode placed in the osmometer and one placed in the outside liquid. The two liquids have a different concentration of ions, and thus form a concentration cell, such as that described on p. 71. Nevertheless, experiment shows that there is no potential difference between these two electrodes. There must, therefore, be a potential difference between the two sides of the membrane, and this *membrane potential* must be equal and opposite to that of the concentration cell, calculated according to the formula given on p. 72.

By special methods it is possible to measure such membrane potentials directly, and the results are of some interest. For further details, see Alexander and Johnson, *Colloid Science.*

2. Dialysis and Membrane Action

As we have seen from our earlier work, small dissolved molecules can pass through a dialysis membrane (parchment paper, collodion, cellophane, pig's bladder, etc.) while molecules large enough to come within the colloidal range are unable to do so. Biltz found that organic dyes pass through a collodion membrane at speeds governed by the number of atoms in the molecules ; in general, where the number of atoms was less than 45, the molecules passed through the membrane rapidly, above 45 they passed through more slowly, from 55 to 70 very slowly or not at all, and above 70 there was no passage of the molecules. Parallel with this decreased rate of diffusion through the membrane, properties characteristic of colloidal solutions become more marked.

These experiments might lead one to believe that the action of the membrane is that of a sieve ; small molecules can get through the openings, but large ones cannot.

On pp. 15 and 16 we have already mentioned some evidence against such a view of membrane action. Other results obtained by Biltz tell against it even more effectively. He showed that the above-mentioned limits were raised if the molecule contained sulphonic acid groups, and lowered, on the other hand, if alizarin residues were present. The size of the molecule itself is not, therefore, a measure of its diffusibility, but the phenomenon is obviously conditioned by physico-chemical properties which run more or less parallel with the molecular weight, but are also connected with the constitution of the molecule. A similar case arises with adsorption, where we have seen that the degree of adsorption increases as the size of the molecule increases, but that it is not entirely governed by this factor, but also varies with the constitution of the molecule (see p. 97).

A special type of dialysis is ultra-filtration, in which colloidal solutions are filtered under pressure through a specially prepared collodion membrane which has been made from collodion dissolved in acetic acid or some other organic solvent. The dispersion medium is separated from the disperse phase, the former passing through the membrane, and the latter not. By modifying the concentration of the collodion, membranes with different properties can be made, so that a given colloid will pass through a certain membrane, but not through another.

In connection with this point it will be clear that no special inference can be drawn concerning the size of colloidal particles from experiments based on ultra-filtration. In this case, also, it is not only the size of the particle that matters, but its constitutive physico-chemical properties which play a part in deciding whether it will pass through the membrane or not.

If the mechanism is not a sieve mechanism, but one in which constitutive properties play a decided part, what theory can be proposed which will allow constitutive influences to be effective ?

All membranes may be regarded as colloidal gels. We have seen in Chapter XI how we may look upon the constitution of a gel. In the pores of the gel there will be, for example, water ; if the substance concerned dissolves in water it will in general be able to pass through the membrane by way of the capillaries. Thus solubility in water plays a part and the available water in the membrane determines the permeability. Now biological membranes are often a special kind of gel ; they are often gelated complex coacervates (see p. 146). We have seen that with these there is an equilibrium between electrical forces and the hydration, in the sense that the electrical forces compress the envelope of water. The complex is thus a mosaic of micelles with water in between. Substances soluble in water can permeate through the water channels. Substances which weaken the electrical repulsion modify the complex in such a way that the water channels become enlarged ; dehydrating substances, on the other hand, should decrease the permeability of substances which are soluble in water.

There is, however, a further complication to be considered. If the substance is strongly adsorbed on the capillary walls of the gel, it cannot pass through the capillaries and the membrane thus shows the property of selective permeability.

The forces of adsorption can be purely electrical. Filter paper (cellulose), for instance, is negatively charged with respect to water. When a ferric oxide sol which, we have learnt, is positively charged, is filtered through thick filter paper, the ferric oxide remains behind on the paper. This is not because the pores of the paper are smaller than the ferric oxide particles ; they are, in fact, many times larger, but the particles are retained by electrical forces. If these particles are discharged, as they can be with sodium hydroxide, they will then readily pass through the paper.

In recent years it has been possible to make membranes which possess an electric charge and which will not allow any ions of a certain sign to pass. These membranes are called cation-selective, or anion-selective membranes according to whether they allow cations or anions to pass.

Summarizing, we may say that solubility in the intermicellar liquid, and adsorption on the gel surface, both play an important part in the mechanism of the semi-permeable membrane, whether it be regarded as an osmotic membrane, as in Chapter I, or as a dialysis membrane.

3. Modern Theories of Electrolytes

On p. 62 we have pointed out that the theory of electrolytes based on the work of Arrhenius, van't Hoff, and Ostwald, is not in all respects satisfactory. This is brought out characteristically by the fact that the Ostwald dilution law (see p. 61) does not hold for strong electrolytes even in very dilute solution.

In order to gain some idea of where the classical theory, which we have dealt with in Chapter III, breaks down, we must first inquire into the data on which the theory is based and the ideas behind it. In the summary below we shall confine our attention to the simplest case, namely an electrolyte of the type of potassium chloride, KCl (which may be written generally as BA), which dissociates at most into two ions. We shall see later how the theory applies to salts such as magnesium chloride, $MgCl_2$ (three ions), aluminium nitrate, $Al(NO_3)_3$ (four ions), etc.

We may sum up then, as follows :

1. The osmotic pressure of a substance dissolved in water (provided it is a non-electrolyte) is directly proportional to the molecular concentration, and is given by the formula $\pi = RTc$ (see p. 13) ; similarly, the lowering of the freezing point, $\Delta' = \Delta c$ (see p. 20).

2. If the dissolved substance is an electrolyte then c in these equations must be replaced by ic.

3. This is due to the fact that the molecules of these substances are dissociated into ions, and these ions behave as entirely separate solute particles.

4. If the degree of dissociation is α then each gram-molecule gives rise to $2\alpha N$ ions and $(1 - \alpha)N$ undissociated molecules. Consequently $i = 1 + \alpha$ (see p. 60).

5. The conductivity is proportional to the ionic concentration. Hence $\alpha = \dfrac{\Lambda_v}{\Lambda_0}$ (see p. 61).

6. If the law of mass action is applied to the equilibrium $BA \rightleftharpoons B^+ + A^-$, the dilution law of Ostwald is obtained.

7. The Nernst equation for the variation of electrode potential with the concentration of the corresponding ion is obeyed when the ionic concentrations obtained by means of 4 and 5 are used.

Clearly the behaviour of electrolytes is determined by the total number of particles—both ions and undissociated molecules—in the solution. This would explain everything if it were a fact that the same values of α were obtained whether it were determined by measurements of electrical conductivity, or of osmotic pressure, lowering of the freezing point, or elevation of the boiling point. For weak electrolytes the values of α obtained by these different methods agree satisfactorily, but for strong electrolytes they only agree to a first approximation ; the deviations exceed the experimental error. This leads directly to the view that the dissociation of molecules into ions does play an important part, and that the classical theory rightly brings the differences between the behaviour of electrolytes and non-electrolytes into relationship with the ionic concentration, but that the theory is too simple.

Many investigators have tried to arrive at a more complete theory in the last fifty years, among them Snethlage, Ghosh, G. N. Lewis, Bjerrum, Brönsted, and particularly Debye and Hückel. Although a conclusive picture has not yet been reached and the new theories are very complicated, we will endeavour to outline the direction in which the solution of the problem is being sought.

The fundamental idea is that the electrical attractions and repulsions between the ions impose limits on their movement and activity as free particles. The force between two ions is given by Coulomb's law as

$z_1 z_2 e^2/Dr^2$, where z_1 and z_2 are the charges on the ions, e is the electronic charge, D the dielectric constant of the medium, and r the distance between the two ions. For weak electrolytes this is not of great importance ; there are but few ions present, so that their mean distance apart is great and the average forces between them correspondingly small. Hence it is only in very accurate work that the classical theory needs to be modified for weak electrolytes. It is a different story for strong electrolytes. Here the classical theory assumes a dissociation into ions amounting to 90 per cent. or more, so that the distance apart of the ions is small, and the electrostatic forces are sufficiently large to exert a considerable effect and must be taken into account. Indeed, at present the general view inclines towards the assumption of almost complete dissociation of strong electrolytes, so that there are only a few undissociated molecules, and no calculation can be correct that does not take into account the electrostatic forces and their consequences.

In order to obtain some idea of the distance apart of the ions, we may, in the first instance, carry out our calculation as follows : suppose there are, say, c ions of potassium and chlorine in 1 c.c. of solution, and these ions are distributed uniformly in a cubic lattice with K^+ and Cl^- ions adjacent to each other, then the distance between two ions will be $\sqrt[3]{\dfrac{1}{c}}$. The distribution cannot, however, be so regular as this, just because the ions are positively and negatively charged. Suppose we consider, for example, a positive ion. In its immediate neighbourhood it is improbable that there will be another positively charged ion, but there will be negatively charged ions. Round about such a positive ion there will therefore exist an " atmosphere " where the density of negative ions increases and that of the positive ions decreases as one approaches the central ion The atmosphere has, therefore, the same type of character as that which we have met on p. 113. Here, however, it is spherically distributed round the ion, whereas on p. 113 the atmosphere is considered above a flat surface.

Debye and Hückel have calculated the " mean distance " apart of two ions under these conditions. This turns out to be not inversely proportional to $\sqrt[3]{c}$, but proportional to $\sqrt{c}$.* In all the following considerations, therefore, this factor, $\sqrt{c}$, occurs.

Because of interionic forces, the effective concentration of each ion is determined by the other ions present, and in the quantitative treatment of phenomena such as ionic equilibria, osmotic pressures and so on, it is necessary to use not ionic concentrations but so-called

* Strictly speaking, the quantity calculated by Debye and Hückel as being proportional to $\sqrt{c}$ is not the mean distance, but another quantity which is, nevertheless, comparable with the r of Coulomb's equation.

ionic activities. These quantities (a) are related to the corresponding concentrations by the equation $a = fc$, where f is the activity coefficient. (For accurate work with non-electrolytes it is similarly necessary to use activities rather than concentrations, but there is then less difference between the two quantities.) Debye and Hückel calculated the activity coefficient f_i of an ion of charge z_i, obtaining the expression :

$$\log f_i = -z_i^2 \left(\frac{e^2}{2DkT}\sqrt{\frac{4\pi e^2}{DkT}\cdot\frac{N}{1000}} \right) \sqrt{\Sigma c_j z_j^2}. \quad . \quad . \quad (2)$$

Here, e is the electronic charge, D the dielectric constant, k the Boltzmann constant, T the absolute temperature, and N the Avogadro number. The summation under the square root sign is taken over all the ions in the solution and is related to the so-called " ionic strength " μ of the solution, which is defined as

$$\mu = \Sigma m_j z_j^2 / 2 \quad . \quad . \quad . \quad . \quad . \quad . \quad (3)$$

Here, m_j is the weight concentration of the jth ion, which in dilute solution is virtually identical with the volume concentration c, (in gm-ions per litre) which we have so far used. Ignoring the small difference between m and c, we may therefore write the above expression for $\log f_i$ in terms of the ionic strength of the solution. (The ionic strength is defined as above, so that for a uni-univalent electrolyte such as NaCl it is numerically equal to the concentration ; for electrolytes of other valency types this is not, of course, the case). When the values of the various constants are substituted into the expression for $\log f_i$ a simple relationship is obtained, which is sufficiently accurate for many purposes :

$$\log_{10} f_i = -0.5\, z_i^2 \sqrt{\mu} \quad . \quad . \quad . \quad . \quad . \quad (4)$$

This holds for aqueous solutions at room temperature and gives reasonably accurate results (as has been shown in a variety of ways) in solutions of ionic strength less than about 0.01. Equation (4) shows that the activity coefficient of an ion depends on (a) its charge and (b) the ionic strength of the solution. It is therefore clear that, to the present approximation, the effect of other ions on the activity coefficient of a given ion is dependent on both their charge and their concentration ; a divalent ion makes a contribution to the ionic strength four times as great as that of a univalent ion present in the same concentration. For more concentrated solutions, the assumptions made in the simple Debye-Hückel treatment are no longer valid, and there are deviations from these expressions. The theory has been extended to higher concentrations, but this work cannot be discussed here. The main point to appreciate is the importance of the ionic strength of the solution in all phenomena involving ions.

Similarly, on the classical theory the contribution of the ions to the conductivity of a solution is assumed to be proportional to their concentrations, so that the degree of dissociation is given by the relationship $\alpha = \Lambda_v/\Lambda_0$. The modern theory, however, assumes that strong electrolytes are completely dissociated, so that $\alpha = 1$ at all concentrations, but that the speed of an ion (and hence its contribution to the conductivity) is reduced by interionic forces, and therefore varies with concentration. Two effects are thought to contribute to this slowing down of the ions, and both depend on the fact that a given ion will always be surrounded by an " ion atmosphere " in which ions of the opposite charge predominate. (This is the same type of " atmosphere " as has been discussed in the case of colloidal particles). The ions making up the atmosphere are continually changing, but the average charge of the atmosphere will always be equal and opposite to that of the central ion, and its " centre of gravity " will coincide with the central ion. Now when the ion moves under an applied electric field, it will take a finite time for the ion atmosphere to re-establish itself, and in the interval the ion will be subject to a retarding force because it will no longer be at the centre of gravity of the ion atmosphere. This is known as the " time of relaxation " effect. Secondly, the ion atmosphere with its attendant water molecules will move in an opposite direction in the field to the ion with its hydration sheath. This introduces an additional viscous effect—the " electrophoretic " effect. Detailed calculations by Debye and Hückel, and later by Onsager and other workers have led to equations which predict the observed dependence of the equivalent conductance on the square root of the concentration.

To return to the subject of ionic equilibria, it should now be clear that, since strong electrolytes are completely dissociated into ions at all concentrations, there is no question of applying the law of mass action. Weak electrolytes produce such a small concentration of ions that for many purposes interionic forces may be neglected and the law of mass action applied, using concentrations. For the most accurate results, however, it is necessary to allow for interionic forces, even in solutions of weak electrolytes, and this is done by writing equilibrium constants in terms of activities instead of concentrations. For instance, the dissociation constant of a weak acid

$$HA \rightleftharpoons H^+ + A^-$$

is strictly :
$$K_a = \frac{a_{H^+} \, a_{A^-}}{a_{HA}} = \frac{[H^+][A^-]}{[HA]} \cdot \frac{f_{H^+} f_{A^-}}{f_{HA}}$$

where the a's are activities and the f's activity coefficients. To quote but two further examples, one should properly work with activity products rather than solubility products of sparingly soluble salts, and the variation of electrode potentials with concentration should for exactness be given in terms of activities. In all this, it will be realized that since activity coefficients (see equation (2)) depend not only on the ionic strength of the solution but also on its dielectric constant, the effects on ionic equilibria both of added ions and of added non-electrolytes which may alter the dielectric constant, are described and summed up by the activity concept.

We may look at this question of ionic equilibria in another way. The simple derivation of the equilibrium constant expression from the law of mass action makes the tacit assumption that the frequency of collisions between molecules or ions is governed purely by chance, and hence is determined by the concentrations of these particles. This may well be true for a gas reaction such as the hydrogen-iodine equilibrium, but in solution it would appear that ions with the same charge would have a decreased chance of colliding and ions with opposite charges an increased chance, because of electrostatic repulsions and attractions. Of course, if we retain the kinetic picture, we may say that this is allowed for by the use of activities rather than concentrations. In fact, however, the kinetic picture is incomplete from quite other points of view, and not only for ionic equilibria. It is well known that the vast majority of chemical reactions involve only binary collisions between the reacting species, that ternary collisions are very rare, and that a reaction never involves the simultaneous collision of more than three particles. Yet the rule for setting up an equilibrium constant is that the concentration of each reactant is raised to a power equal to the number of molecules of it appearing in the equation— which on the kinetic picture implies that this number of molecules is concerned in the collisions leading to reaction. As a matter of fact, equilibrium constant expressions can be rigorously derived—in the form in which we have already met them—on quite different grounds from the above kinetic ones, so that the ultimate validity of such expressions does not depend on any doubtful assumptions of a kinetic nature.

4. Enzymes

Reference has been made on p. 43 to the fact that systems involving enzymes are heterogeneous systems. It is proposed here to consider further the physical chemistry of enzymes.

Enzymes are catalysts which play a very important part in many chemical reactions occurring in living organisms. Enzymes are known which will catalyse the hydrolysis of esters, such as fats, the hydrolysis of disaccharides, the breaking of peptide linkages in proteins, and the transference of hydrogen from one molecule to another, and so on.

It was at first thought that enzymes must be actually present in living cells if they were to be effective, i.e. if they were separated from the living cell they would be inactive. This view was disposed of by Buchner in 1897, who showed that the contents of the yeast cell when expressed from the living cells would catalyse alcoholic fermentation. Enzymes must therefore be looked upon as compounds which are capable of existence and of being active in the absence of living material. Possibly the best definition of an enzyme is that given by Waldschmidt-Leitz : an enzyme is a catalyst of an organic nature with a specific activity, formed only by living cells, but capable of acting independently of them.

The precise nature of enzymes is still in doubt. Some of them, such as urease, pepsin, and trypsin, have been prepared in the crystalline state, but it has not been proved that in every case the crystals are identical with the enzyme. Enzymes are highly specific in their catalytic effect ; a given enzyme will usually catalyse only one particular reaction or type of reaction. Enzymes are protein molecules, often joined (or " conjugated ") to a non-protein part sometimes known as the " prosthetic group." Broadly speaking, the prosthetic group seems to be responsible for the catalytic activity, and the protein part for the specificity. However, the absence of the protein part always reduces the activity of the prosthetic group, so the distinction of function cannot be complete.

If enzymes are catalysts they should not be used up in the course of the reaction, nor should they affect the equilibrium constant of the reaction they catalyse. Thus it follows that enzymes—like other catalysts—must affect the rate of forward and reverse reactions to an equal extent. This conclusion has been verified in some cases where it was possible to carry out the necessary experiments.

Enzymes are affected very markedly by a number of conditions. They are sensitive to temperature, to the pH of the medium in which they are acting, to the concentration of the substance they are acting upon (this is called the substrate), and to the presence of other compounds such as certain electrolytes. Like other catalysts they are readily poisoned.

Effect of temperature. All enzymes are greatly affected by change of temperature. For each enzyme there is an optimum temperature range over which it is most active, although this temperature is not clearly defined for each particular enzyme. It depends to some extent on the previous history of the enzyme, on its purity, and on the pH of the medium. All enzymes become inactive when they are boiled in aqueous solution for a few minutes. This inactivation lent support to the idea that enzymes were intimately connected with living material and were only effective when in the presence of living matter, for boiling would kill the living substance. It is now believed, however, that the effect of boiling is to denature (see p. 155) the protein portion of the enzyme, which thereby loses its specific structure ; apparently this structure is essential for the enzymatic activity.

Effect of pH of the medium. The activity of enzymes depends very markedly on the pH of the medium in which the reaction occurs. All enzymes have an optimum pH at which they are most effective. Indeed this method has been used to determine the pH of a solution.

For some enzymes, such as invertase, the maximum activity comes at a pH corresponding to the isoelectric point of the protein part of the enzyme.

Effect of concentration of substrate. It is a well-known fact that the fermentation of glucose by means of zymase takes place best at an optimum concentration of glucose. If the concentration of glucose is too great fermentation is considerably slowed down. Also, if the concentration of alcohol becomes too high the fermentation stops.

In general there appears to be a limiting rate of reaction as the concentration of the substrate increases. Various theories have been proposed to explain this, none of which is perfectly satisfactory. The simplest explanation is that enzymes are effective because of adsorption ; the reacting substances are adsorbed on the surface of the enzyme where they react, and the products are desorbed. It is clear that once the enzyme surface has become saturated the rate of reaction will reach a limiting value. Others have assumed reversible compound formation between the enzyme and the substrate in place of adsorption. The formation of this compound would be governed by the law of mass action, and a state of equilibrium would be reached. It would, however, be difficult to distinguish this state of affairs from that in which the substrate has been adsorbed, because both phenomena lead to exactly the same kinetic equations.

LIST OF TEXT-BOOKS FOR FURTHER READING

General Physical Chemistry

Physical Chemistry. A. J. Mee. (Heinemann.)
Test-book of Physical Chemistry. S. Glasstone. (Macmillan/Van Nostrand.)
Elements of Physical Chemistry. S. Glasstone. (Macmillan/Van Nostrand.)
Structure of Physical Chemistry. C. N. Hinshelwood. (O.U.P.)

Chemical Kinetics

Kinetics of Chemical Change. C. N. Hinshelwood. (O.U.P.)
Chemical Kinetics. K. J. Laidler. (McGraw Hill.)

Electrochemistry

Electrochemistry of Solutions. S. Glasstone. (Methuen.)
Introduction to Electrochemistry. S. Glasstone. (Macmillan/Van Nostrand.)
Electrochemistry (2 vols.). " Kortum-Bockris." (Elsevier.)

Colloids

Colloid Science (2 vols.). H. R. Kruyt. (Elsevier.)
Colloid Science. Alexander and Johnson. (O.U.P.)
Physics and Chemistry of Surfaces. N. K. Adam. (O.U.P.)
Electrical Phenomena at Interfaces. Ed. J. A. V. Butler. (Methuen.)

High Polymers

Chemistry of High Polymers. C. E. H. Bawn. (Butterworth.)
High Polymers. A series edited by H. Mark. (Interscience.)

EXAMPLES

CHAPTER I

(1) What is the partial pressure of the oxygen in a mixture of two parts by weight of oxygen and one part by weight of helium at a total pressure of 1 atmosphere ?

(2) Will deuterium (hydrogen of atomic weight 2) diffuse through the walls of a porous pot faster or slower than ordinary hydrogen ? Calculate the ratio of the two rates of diffusion.

(3) Explain why diffusion takes place in a definite direction although it is based on the Brownian movement which has no definite direction.

(4) Two large vessels are connected by a tube of length 10 cm. and cross-section 3 sq. mm. One vessel is filled with a solution of cane sugar containing 50 gm. per litre, the other with water, and the tube with a mixture of both. After some weeks a stationary state is reached when the sugar diffuses at a constant speed from the first to the second vessel. Assuming that convection is completely avoided and concentration differences in the large vessels are neglected, calculate how much sugar diffuses from the one vessel to the other if the diffusion constant of cane sugar is 0·3 sq. cm. per day.

(5) What is the osmotic pressure of a 1·71 weight per cent. solution of cane sugar at 37° C. ? What is the freezing point depression of the solution ? (Molecular weight of cane sugar = 342 ; depression constant for water 18·6°.)

(6) A solution of cane sugar (molecular weight 342) containing 1 gm. per litre has an osmotic pressure of 75 cm. The density of the solution is 1 gm. per ml. Calculate the value of the gas constant R in c.g.s. units. The acceleration due to gravity is 980 cm. per sec. per sec.

(7) What must be the concentration of an aqueous solution of common salt if it is to be isotonic with a solution of this substance which freezes at − 0·0186° C. ?

(8) An aqueous solution of sugar boils at 100.100° C. under 1 atmos. pressure. What is the osmotic pressure of this solution at 25° C. ? (Molecular elevation for water = 5·0° ; 1 gm. mol. of an ideal gas at 1 atm. pressure and 25° C. occupies a volume of 22·4 litres. The density of the sugar solution may be taken as 1 gm. per ml.)

(9) Calculate the vapour pressure at 22° C. of a 0·1 N solution of sodium sulphate. The density of the solution may be taken as 1 gm. per ml. The vapour pressure of water at 22° C. is 20·0 mm.

(10) How many litres of ethanol must be added to 1 litre of water so that the mixture shall freeze at − 5·0° C. ? (Molecular depression for water = 18·6° ; density of ethanol = 0·80 gm. per ml.)

(11) A solution of 5·664 gm. of sulphur in 100 ml. of carbon disulphide boils at a temperature 0·411° higher than pure carbon disulphide. What is the molecular formula of the dissolved sulphur ? (Molecular elevation for carbon disulphide = 23·4° ; density of carbon disulphide = 1·263 gm. per ml.)

CHAPTER II

(1) In a chemical reaction it is found that after 1 hour, one-half, after 2 hours, three-quarters, and after 3 hours, seven-eighths of the starting material had been decomposed. What is the order of the reaction ?

(2) The thermal decomposition of gaseous acetaldehyde proceeds as follows :

Time (minutes) . . .	0	3	6	12	18	48	138
Partial pressure of acetalde-hyde (mm.) . . .	250	200	167	125	100	50	20

Is this a first-order or a second-order reaction ? What is the velocity constant ?

(3) The radiation from a radioactive preparation falls to one-third after 12 hours. How long will it be before the radiation is reduced to a thousandth ? After how long will the radiation be zero ?

(4) Draw a graph showing how the velocity of the reaction and the yield of an autocatalytic reaction, e.g. the reaction between permanganate and oxalic acid, depend on time.

(5) Can Q_{10} have a value less than unity ? Can it be less than zero ?

(6) The decomposition of acetone dicarboxylic acid at 27° C. is sixteen times as rapid as at 7° C. What is the value of Q_{10} for this reaction ? If the Arrhenius law holds accurately for this reaction what is the ratio of the reaction velocities at 127° C. and 147° C. ?

(7) The energy of activation of the reaction

$$2HI \rightarrow H_2 + I_2 - 10,000 \text{ cal.}$$

is 44,000 cal. Is the value of Q_{10} for the reaction

$$H_2 + I_2 \rightarrow 2HI + 10,000 \text{ cal.}$$

greater or less than that of the first reaction ?

(8) If a mixture of 3 volumes of hydrogen and 1 volume of nitrogen is heated at 480° C. and 1 atmosphere pressure for a long time, the ammonia produced occupies 1% by volume of the mixture. What is the value of the equilibrium constant? What percentage of ammonia should be formed if the pressure is increased to 108·9 atmospheres ?

(9) At 1,000° C. and a pressure of 15 atmospheres the equilibrium constant of the reaction

$$CO_2 \text{ (gas)} + C \text{ (solid)} \rightleftharpoons 2CO \text{ (gas)}$$

is such that for every 9 moles of carbon monoxide there is 1 mole of carbon dioxide.

(a) Would the equilibrium be displaced if nitrogen were pumped into the vessel until the pressure was 30 atmospheres ?

(b) For what pressure of the mixture (now without nitrogen) is the ratio $CO : CO_2 = 4 : 1$. The temperature remains at 1,000° C.

(10) A mixture of equal volumes of carbon dioxide and hydrogen is heated to 1,000° C. at 0·1 atmosphere. After attainment of equilibrium the composition of the mixture by volume is CO_2, 33·3 per cent.; H_2, 33·3 per cent.; CO, 16·67 per cent.; H_2O, 16·67 per cent.

(a) What would these percentages become if the total pressure were 1 atmosphere ?

(b) The equilibrium constant of the dissociation of water at 100° C. is

$$\frac{(p_{H_2})^2(p_{O_2})}{(p_{H_2O})^2} = 1·44 \times 10^{-20} \text{ atmospheres.}$$

What is the equilibrium constant for the dissociation of CO_2 into CO and O_2 at 1,000° C. ?

(11) At 350° C. and a total pressure of 1 atmosphere nitrogen dioxide is 20 per cent. decomposed into nitric oxide and oxygen. Calculate the equilibrium constant. Does the percentage decomposition increase with increasing total pressure ? At what total pressure should the nitrogen dioxide be half decomposed at this temperature ?

(12) When sodium vapour is added to a mixture of chlorine and hydrogen at 1 atmosphere pressure and room temperature a chain reaction is started. When 1 mg. of sodium is added 1,000 litres of chlorine and hydrogen are converted into hydrogen chloride. How long is the reaction chain ?

(13) A mixture of equimolecular quantities of ethyl alcohol and acetic acid is prepared. Immediately after mixing, 10 ml. of the mixture were neutralized by 100 ml. of N NaOH. When the mixture reaches equilibrium 10 ml. requires 40 ml. of N NaOH for neutralization. What is the equilibrium constant for the formation of the ester ? After the first titration the red colour of the phenolphthalein used as indicator remains for some time, whereas after the second titration it speedily disappears. Explain this.

(14) What is the effect of increasing temperature and pressure on the speed of the reaction for the formation of ammonia from nitrogen and hydrogen ?

(15) When steam is passed over heated coke the following reactions take place :

$$H_2O + C \rightleftharpoons CO + H_2$$
$$C + CO_2 \rightleftharpoons 2CO$$
$$C + 2H_2 \rightleftharpoons CH_4$$
$$CO + H_2O \rightleftharpoons CO_2 + H_2$$

At 1 atmosphere pressure and at 600° C. and 700° C. respectively, the percentage composition of the mixture by volume was as follows :

	CO	H_2	CO_2	CH_4	H_2O
600° C.	15	38	20	8	19
700° C.	34	45	9	4	8

Which of the above mentioned reactions are exothermic and which are endothermic ?

(16) The position of the equilibrium ethanol + acetic acid $\rightleftharpoons$ ethyl acetate + water is not affected by temperature. What can you conclude about the heat of reaction ? How would the speed of hydrolysis of ethyl acetate with much water be affected by increase of temperature ?

(17) Nitrogen dioxide in the gaseous state is partly associated to N_2O_4. At 27° C. and 1 atmosphere 3·12 gm. of the gas occupy 1 litre. At 111° C. and the same pressure the volume is 2·04 litres.

(a) What is the degree of dissociation at 27° C. ?

(b) At which of the two temperatures is the dissociation the greater ?

(c) Is the dissociation exothermic or endothermic ?

(d) Suppose the gas is heated to 111° C. not at constant pressure but at constant volume. Is the pressure then greater than, equal to, or less than 2·04 atmospheres ?

(18) The reaction $C + CO_2 \rightleftharpoons 2CO$ is slightly endothermic to the right. When oxygen at 1 atmosphere pressure is blown through a red-hot bed of coke at 800° C. the mixture produced contains 8 volumes of CO and 1 volume of CO_2. If air is used instead of oxygen must the temperature of the coke be higher or lower than 800° C. in order to maintain the same proportion of CO to CO_2 ? Assume that nitrogen does not react with coke and that the oxygen is completely converted into oxides of carbon, and that steady equilibrium has been reached.

(19) Explain why the radioactivity of a radium preparation first increases and then remains practically constant (radioactive equilibrium).

CHAPTER III

(1) A current of 1 amp. deposits 0·001118 gm. silver per second. The atomic weight of silver is 107.880. Calculate the value of the Faraday (F).

(2) In the discharge of the lead accumulator the reaction at the positive plate may be represented approximately as

$$PbO_2 + 4H^+ + SO_4^{--} + 2e \rightarrow PbSO_4 + 2H_2O$$

and at the negative plate

$$Pb + SO_4^{--} \rightarrow PbSO_4 + 2e.$$

What is the least weight of lead dioxide and the least number of gram-molecules of sulphuric acid that the accumulator must contain if it is to provide a current of 1 amp. for 30 hours ?

(1 Faraday = 96,000 coulombs ; Pb = 208.)

(3) A direct current is passed through equal volumes of a dilute and a concentrated solution of copper sulphate in series. All electrodes are of platinum and are of the same surface area. They are at the same distance apart in the two solutions.

(a) Is gas evolved from one or more electrodes ? If so, from which electrode is most gas evolved ?

(b) Is copper deposited at one or more of the electrodes ?

the wires are connected ? What happens if (a) only an iron wire, and (b) only a platinum wire, is placed in the solution ?

(21) A silver electrode and a glass electrode are placed in a 0·1 N solution of hydrochloric acid. The solution is now titrated with N silver nitrate until a considerable excess of silver is present. Show by means of a graph how the potential between the two electrodes changes during the titration. (Make the x axis the number of ml. of silver nitrate added, and the y axis the e.m.f.). [Solubility product of silver chloride $= 10^{-10}$; $RT/F \log_{10} e = 0·058$ v.]

(22) A mixture of acetic acid and ammonium chloride dissolved in water is titrated with sodium hydroxide and during the titration the pH is measured. Show graphically how the pH changes as a function of the added sodium hydroxide, and show how, from the titration curve, it is possible to obtain the quantities of the two components present in the mixture. The dissociation constants of acetic acid and ammonia may both be taken as 10^{-5}. How is the titration curve modified when hydrochloric acid is present in addition to the acetic acid and the ammonium chloride ?

(23) The solubility of magnesium fluoride is 0·075 gm. per litre. What is the solubility product ?

(24) The solubility products of silver chloride and silver iodide are 10^{-10} and 10^{-16} respectively. What happens when silver chloride is added to 0·1 M potassium iodide, and when silver iodide is added to 0·1 M potassium chloride ?

(25) Does the pH of (a) 0·01 N sodium hydroxide, (b) 0·01 N hydrochloric acid increase with rise of temperature ?

(26) Which has the greater osmotic pressure, a solution of hydrochloric acid of pH 3 or a solution of acetic acid of pH 3 ? Which of these solutions has the greater specific conductivity and which has the greater equivalent conductivity ? [$\lambda_{H^+} = 350$; $\lambda_{Cl^-} = 76$; $\lambda_{CH_3COO^-} = 41$].

CHAPTER IV

(1) Benzoic acid is to be extracted from an aqueous solution by shaking with benzene. Is the pH of the aqueous layer affected by this process ?

(2) The distribution coefficient of iodine between carbon disulphide and water is 500. A potassium iodide solution containing 0·05 mol. per litre is shaken with iodine and carbon disulphide until equilibrium is reached. On titration with thiosulphate the concentration of the iodine in the aqueous layer was 0·0206 moles per litre, and in the carbon disulphide layer it was 0·3 moles per litre. In the potassium iodide solution part of the iodine reacts with iodide ions to give I_3^- ions. Calculate the equilibrium constant of the reaction $I^- + I_2 \rightleftharpoons I_3^-$ assuming that KI and KI_3 do not dissolve in carbon disulphide.

(3) Langmuir obtained the following figures for the adsorption of methane on 6,750 sq. cm. of mica at 90° K.

Pressure (dynes/sq. cm.)	Adsorption (gm. mol.)
0·484	2×10^{-7}
1·31	5×10^{-7}
3·06	10×10^{-7}
9·2	20×10^{-7}
15·3	25×10^{-7}
27·6	30×10^{-7}
∞	40×10^{-7} (extrapolated)

Do these figures conform to the Langmuir isotherm ?   Calculate the maximum adsorption in molecules per sq. cm. ($N = 6 \times 10^{23}$).   Calculate the surface occupied by a molecule of methane at the maximum adsorption. How could one obtain answers to these questions if the value of the adsorption at infinite pressure were not given ?

(4) A 10-litre vessel is full of saturated water vapour at 21° C., the pressure being 19 mm. ; 100 mg. of silica gel are added, when the pressure falls to 10 mm.   A further 100 mg. of silica gel are added and the pressure becomes 5 mm.   After another 500 mg. of silica gel are added the pressure is 1 mm., and when a total of 4 gm. of silica gel has been added the pressure is 0·1 mm.

With the help of these figures obtain the adsorption isotherm of water on silica gel.   One mole of water vapour occupies 2,500 litres at 21° C. and 7·6 mm. pressure.

(5) A closed vessel of capacity 100 litres contains 100 mg. of a gas.   A second vessel of 10 litres capacity contains 10 mg. of the same gas at the same temperature ; 1 gm. of activated carbon is added to both vessels. In which vessel is most gas adsorbed ?

(6) 10 gm. of activated carbon are added to a solution of a dye containing 1 gm. per litre.   The concentration is reduced to 0·1 gm. per litre. If 109 gm. of the same carbon are added to a litre of a solution which contains 10 gm. of the same dye find out whether less than 90 per cent., 90–95 per cent., 95–98 per cent., or more than 99 per cent. of the dye is adsorbed.

(7) How can water be softened with the aid of ion exchange reagents ? What factors affect the quantity of water softened by a given amount of ion exchanger ?   How can the exchanger be regenerated ?

(8) Show that for the ionic exchange of hydrogen and calcium ions

$$\frac{(X_H)^2}{(X_{Ca})} = k \frac{(C_H)^2}{(C_{Ca})}$$

where X_H and X_{Ca} are the masses of the H^+ and Ca^{++} ions adsorbed respectively from solutions containing concentrations of H^+ and Ca^{++} ions C_H and C_{Ca} respectievly.

CHAPTER V

(1) Between two vessels filled with 0·001 N potassium chloride solution is a porous plug of silver chloride, the pores being filled with the solution. A direct current flows through the two vessels in series. Does the liquid move, and if so, in what direction ?

When 0·1 N potassium chloride is used in place of the 0·001 N solution and the same potential is applied, is the flow of liquid stronger or weaker ? What differences would there be if silver nitrate were used in place of potassium chloride ?

(2) The streaming potential through a quartz capillary with a solution of aluminium chloride of concentration 1 micromole per litre is brought to zero. What would an electro-endosmosis experiment with the same capillary and the same aluminium chloride solution show ?

(3) In the carrying out of an electrophoresis experiment with the apparatus shown in Fig. 40 it is necessary to choose a suitable liquid above the suspension. In determining the electrophoretic velocity of ferric hydroxide particles suspended in very dilute hydrochloric acid, what is the most suitable from among the following liquids : 0·001 N HCl, 0·1 N NaCl, or the liquid in which the ferric hydroxide is suspended, which has been separated from the ferric hydroxide by centrifuging ?

(4) What are the potential determining ions for barium sulphate, lead chromate, zinc sulphide, silver, platinum ?

CHAPTER VI

(1) Calculate the osmotic pressure of a 1 per cent. solution of rubber in benzene with respect to pure benzene if the molecular weight of rubber is 50,000. How much higher does the rubber solution stand in the osmometer than the benzene outside ? The density of the solution is 0·8 gm. per ml. at 27° C.

(2) Calculate the sedimentation velocity of the particles of a gold sol in water if the particles are spherical and have a radius of 4 mμ. How long will it take for the particles to reach the bottom of an ultracentrifuge when the centrifugal field is 250,000 times as strong as gravity and the cell is 1 cm. high. The viscosity of water is 0·01 c.g.s. and the density of gold is 19 gm. per ml.

(3) Which of the following are hydrophobic and which are hydrophilic colloids : gum arabic in water, silver chloride in water, silica in water, platinum in water, hæmoglobin in dilute acid, rubber in benzene, sodium chloride in benzene, sodium oleate in water, triolein (glyceryl oleate) in water, starch ?

CHAPTER VII

(1) An aluminium hydroxide sol can just be precipitated by the addition of potassium chloride to a final concentration of 80 millimol. per litre. The addition of potassium oxalate to a concentration of 0·4 millimol. per litre

causes complete precipitation. Are the particles positively or negatively charged? What concentration of calcium chloride would be required for precipitation ?

(2) A silver iodide sol moves towards the cathode in electrophoresis. Show by means of a graph the effect of the addition of increasing concentrations of potassium sulphate, barium nitrate, and potassium iodide on the electrophoretic velocity of the sol.

(3) A silver iodide sol is prepared by mixing 0·05 N sodium iodide solution and silver nitrate solution, the sodium iodide being always in excess. The sol is then placed in a dialyser taking care that the level of the dialysing liquid (distilled water) and the sol are the same. Explain the fact that the level of the sol first rises and then falls. What is the maximum rise ?

(4) Can a hydrophobic sol be stable and at the same time have a zero electrophoretic velocity ? Can a hydrophobic sol show electrophoresis in an electric field and still be stable ?

(5) Why is it that when hydrogen sulphide is passed into a solution of arsenious oxide (solubility 20 gm. per litre) a sol is formed, whereas when hydrogen sulphide is passed into a solution of arsenious chloride, $AsCl_3$, which is 1 N with hydrochloric acid, such as one meets in qualitative analysis, a precipitate is formed ?

CHAPTER VIII

(1) How may the molecular weight of rubber $(C_5H_8)_x$ be determined ?

(2) A 2 per cent. solution has an osmotic pressure with respect to the pure solvent of 0·0023 atmospheres, and a specific viscosity, $(\eta_s - \eta_0)/\eta_0$ of 3. What do these data indicate about the nature of the solute ? What is its molecular weight ? What would the nature of the substance be if the specific viscosity were not 3 but 0·05 ? The density of the solute and of the solvent may be regarded as 1 gm. per ml.

(3) Nylon is a poly-condensation product of adipic acid

$$(COOH.(CH_2)_4.COOH)$$

and 1 : 6-diaminohexane. Is nylon a chain or a network molecule ?

CHAPTER IX

(1) Draw a graph showing the relation between the viscosity of a 1 per cent. solution of gelatin at pH 3 and the concentration (in milli-equivalents per litre) of the undermentioned salts which (separately) are added to the gelatin solution : barium chloride, potassium ferricyanide, lanthanum sulphate, magnesium sulphate, sodium chloride.

(2) What are the resemblances and the differences between the coagulation of a hydrophobic colloid and that of a protein ?

(3) The isoelectric point of the protamines (a kind of protein) is at pH 12, i.e., it is abnormally high. What conclusions can be drawn about the chemical composition of protamines ?

(4) A solution of a protein can be brought to different pH values by the addition of sodium hydroxide or hydrochloric acid. In what pH range (or ranges) would such a solution have a buffering action ?

(5) Isotonic solutions of the following in water are provided : (1) sodium acetate, (2) 0·1 N hydrochloric acid, (3) glucose, (4) a protein in a buffer of pH 4. Arrange the solutions in ascending order of osmotic pressure, freezing point, specific conductivity, pH, and viscosity.

(6) How may the electrophoretic velocity of a protein be measured ?

(7) How could a mixture of two proteins be separated into its constituents ?

(8) What happens in mixtures of :

(a) a negatively charged gelatin sol and a negatively charged gold sol ;

(b) a positively charged gelatin sol and a negatively charged gold sol ;

(c) a negatively charged gelatin sol and a negatively charged gum arabic sol ;

(d) a positively charged gelatin sol and a negatively charged gum arabic sol ?

(9) What happens when solutions of pepsin and chymopepsin (proteins with isoelectric points at pH 2 and pH 8 respectively) are mixed at pH 5 ? How does the mixture react to the addition of hydrochloric acid, sodium chloride, barium chloride, aluminium sulphate, lanthanum chloride, and potassium sulphate ?

(10) Arrange in order the concentrations (in gm. equivalents per litre) of the following salts which would just neutralize the complex coacervation between gum arabic and gelatin : potassium chloride, potassium ferrocyanide, barium chloride, aluminium sulphate, lanthanum chloride, and potassium sulphate.

Can complex coacervation also be hindered by the addition of acid or alkali ?

(11) By what methods can a silver iodide sol be made so that it is not coagulated by the addition of potassium nitrate solution up to a final concentration of M/2 ?

(12) Does the order of mixing of a gold sol, a gelatin solution and a fairly concentrated solution of common salt have any effect on the ultimate result of the experiment ?

CHAPTER X

(1) Is there any relation between the detergent action of soap and the colloidal properties of soap solutions ?

(2) Why should soap be useful as a stabilizing agent for emulsions of oil in water ? In an emulsion the oil is dispersed in the form of very small droplets in the water.

(3) Explain the fact that salts of fatty acids with less than eight carbon atoms do not function as soaps.

CHAPTER XI

(1) Show graphically the connection between the pressure difference and the velocity with which a viscous liquid (e.g. glycerol or asphalt) and a dilute gel can be forced through a pipe. How would the graph appear for a thixotropic ferric oxide sol ?

(2) Why does unvulcanized rubber dissolve in benzene whilst vulcanized rubber only swells ?

(3) Why does rubber become more stiff and at the same time less elastic in proportion as the rubber is vulcanized with more sulphur ?

(4) Show graphically the swelling of gelatin as a function of pH. How does the curve change when at each pH an equal quantity of common salt is added ?

CHAPTER XII

(1) What is understood by *specific* electrical conductivity and by *equivalent* electrical conductivity of an electrolyte ?
Do they increase or decrease with dilution, and why ?

(2) If it is desired to find the molecular weight of a protein by osmotic pressure determinations is it necessary to use a membrane which allows only the solvent (water) to pass through, or may small ions be allowed to pass ? At what pH is it best to work ? Is it desirable to add much or little salt ?

(3) A cation-selective membrane separates two sodium chloride solutions from each other. The concentrations are 0·1 and 0·01 N respectively. Will the water molecules pass from one solution to the other, and if so, in which direction ?
Do the sodium and the chloride ions pass through, and if so, in what direction ?
Would an electric current pass if a potential difference were applied between the two solutions ?

ANSWERS

CHAPTER I

1. 0·2 atmosphere.
2. Slower ; 1 : 1·4.
4. 0·315 mg.
5. 1·27 atmosphere ; 0·093°.
6. 8·38 × 10⁷ ergs per degree.
7. 0·292 gm. per litre.
8. 4·8 atmospheres.
9. 19·46 mm.
10. 0·155 litres.
11. S_8.

CHAPTER II

1. First order.
2. Second order ; 3·3 × 10⁻⁴ mm⁻¹min⁻¹.
3. After 75·5 hours ; after an infinitely long time.
5. Only very rarely (e.g. for enzyme reactions at the denaturizing temperature) ; no.
6. $Q_{10} = 4$; $k_{147} = k_{127}$.
7. Smaller.
8. 1·01 × 10³ (atmosphere)² ; 40 per cent.
9. (a) No ; (b) at 38 atmospheres.
10 (a) 33·3 per cent. CO_2, 33·3 per cent. H_2, 16·7 per cent. CO and 16·7 per cent. H_2O ; (b) 9 × 10⁻²² atmospheres.
11. 0·0057 atmosphere ; decreases ; at 0·028 atmosphere.
12. 10⁶ links.
13. $k = 2·25$.
14. Both increase the speed.
15. $H_2O + C \rightarrow CO + H_2$, endothermic ;
    $C + CO_2 \rightarrow 2CO$, endothermic ;
    $C + 2H_2 \rightarrow CH_4$, exothermic ;
    $CO + H_2O \rightarrow CO_2 + H_2$, exothermic.
16. Heat of reaction is zero ; speed of hydrolysis increases with rise of temperature.
17. (a) 20 per cent. ;
    (b) At 111° ;
    (c) Endothermic ;
    (d) Less than 2·04 atmospheres.
18. Lower than 800°.
19. In the first phase the radiation from the disintegration products is added to that of the preparation, but these products disintegrate rapidly.

CHAPTER III

1. 96,494 coulombs.
2. 135 gm. PbO_2 and $1·125$ gm. mol. H_2SO_4.
3. (a) At both anodes equally ;
   (b) At both cathodes equally ;
   (c) Both solutions become warmer, the more dilute becoming the warmer.
4. (a) The anode is $58·32$ mg. lighter, and the cathode is heavier by the same amount ;
   (b) Increased ;
   (c) Transport number of the silver ion is 4/9.
5. (a) $3·24$ gm. heavier.
   (b) 336 c.c. hydrogen at the platinum cathode, and 168 c.c. oxygen at the platinum anode.
   (c) $0·8$.
7. $1·36 \times 10^{-5}$.
8. $1·35 \times 10^{-8}$.
9. $0·1$ N HCl, $0·09$ N HCl $+ 0·1$ N acetic acid ; $0·1$ N acetic acid.
10. pH $= 3$, $K = 10^{-5}$.
11. $K = 1·6 \times 10^{-5}$; weak ; smaller.
12. pH $= 1·4$; 12.85 ; $10·48$;
    $[H^+] = 5 \times 10^{-4}$; 7×10^{-5} ; $2·5 \times 10^{-11}$;
    $[OH^-] = 2 \times 10^{-11}$; $1·4 \times 10^{-10}$; 4×10^{-4}.
13. pH $= 2·7$; 1.
14. pH $= 0$; $1·5$; $13·3$; $2·5$.
15. pH $= 10$; 4 ; 7.
16. pH $= 2$ by diluting $0·1$ N HCl ten times with water.
    pH $= 5$ by mixing 2 volumes of $0·1$ N NaOH with 3 volumes of $0·1$ N ammonia.
    pH $= 8$ by mixing 15 volumes of $0·1$ N HCl with 16 volumes of $0·1$ N ammonia.
    pH $= 12$ by diluting $0·1$ N NaOH ten times with water.
17. Chiefly the hydrochloric acid ; pH $= 3$.
18. pH $= 6·67$.
19. $0·464$ volt ; that in the HCl ; $H^+ + OH^- \rightarrow H_2O$.
20. A current flows from the platinum to the iron electrode ; Fe^{+++} is thus reduced to Fe^{++} and Fe goes into solution as Fe^{++}. With simply an iron wire practically all the Fe^{+++} would be converted into Fe^{++} by the reaction $2Fe^{+++} + Fe \rightarrow 3Fe^{++}$. With simply a platinum wire nothing happens.
23. 7×10^{-9}.
24. $AgCl + I^- \rightarrow AgI + Cl^-$ until $C_{Cl^-} = 10^6 C_{I^-}$, or all the AgCl is dissolved ; $AgI + Cl^- \rightarrow AgCl + I^-$ until $C_{I^-} = 10^{-7}$N.
25. The pH of NaOH decreases ; that of the HCl remains constant.
26. The acetic acid ; the hydrochloric acid ; the hydrochloric acid.

CHAPTER IV

1. Yes.
2. 1,111 litres per mole.
3. 24 A^2 ; from the adsorption at two different pressures the two constants of the Langmuir isotherm can be calculated.
5. In the first.
6. 98–99 per cent.
7. The number of exchangeable cations in the exchanger and the hardness of the water. By passing brine over the exchanger.
8. Assuming the ion exchanger to be RH then
$$2RH + Ca^{++} \rightleftharpoons R_2Ca + 2H^+$$
whereby the law of mass action gives
$$\frac{[H^+]^2 . (X_{Ca})}{[Ca^{++}]^2 . (X_H)}$$

CHAPTER V

1. At the cathode ; weaker ; movement towards the anode.
2. No movement.
3. The last mentioned.
4. Ba^{++}, SO_4^{--} ; Pb^{++}, CrO_4^{--} ; Zn^{++}, S^{--} ; Ag^+, H^+, OH^- ; H^+, OH^-.

CHAPTER VI

1. $4\cdot9 \times 10^{-3}$ atmospheres ; $6\cdot4$ cm.
2. $6\cdot4 \times 10^{-8}$ cm. per sec. $= 0\cdot055$ mm. per day ; 62^5 sec.
3. AgCl, SiO_2, Pt, NaCl, triolein are hydrophobic ; the others are hydrophilic.

CHAPTER VII

1. Positive ; 40 millimoles per litre.
4. No ; yes.
5. In the second case the HCl causes coagulation of the particles.

CHAPTER VIII

1. By dissolving in benzene and determining the osmotic pressure ; with the ultracentrifuge by viscosity determinations.
2. It is a lyophilic chain colloid ; 200,000 ; spherical colloid.
3. Chain colloid.

CHAPTER IX

3. They possess many basic groups.
4. Where the pH is in the neighbourhood of the negative logarithm of the dissociation constants of the acidic and the basic groups.

5. Osmotic pressure and freezing point are the same for all ; 3, 4, 1, 2 ; 2, 4, 3, 1 ; 1 = 2, 3, 4.
7. By salting out ; by electrophoresis.
8. (a) Protection ;
   (b) Coagulation ;
   (c) Nothing ;
   (d) Eventually complex coacervation.
9. Complex coacervation. Goes into solution.
10. $KCl > K_2SO_4 > K_4Fe(CN)_6$ and $KCl > BaCl_2 > LaCl_3 > Al_2(SO_4)_3$; yes.
11. By adding protecting colloids.
12. Yes.

CHAPTER X

1. Yes.
2. By adsorption the droplets become charged.
3. No micelle formation, too little adsorption.

CHAPTER XI

2. Vulcanization gives sulphur bridges between the molecules. They form a continuous network.
3. The network becomes stiffer.

CHAPTER XII

1. Specific conductivity increases with increasing concentration. Equivalent conductivity decreases with decreasing dissociation and/or increasing interaction between the ions.
2. The small ions may pass through ; at the isoelectric point ; much salt.
3. Water passes into the concentrated solution. Cl^- cannot pass through the membrane, and the Na^+ also does not pass through ; yes, because the sodium ions can carry the current through the membrane.

INDEX